let me go on

Paul Griffiths

 HENNINGHAM
FAMILY
PRESS

First published in 2023 by Henningham Family Press
130 Sandringham Road, London, E8 2HJ
henninghamfamilypress.com

Printed and bound by Short Run Press, Exeter
& Henningham Family Press, London

ISBN | 9781916218673

G . F
SMITH
1885 ONWARDS

let me go on

Paul Griffiths

HENNINGHAM FAMILY PRESS

London

2023

for Anne

* * * *

Well, I did go.

I was out there in the snow.

I have to say it was beauteous, if harsh.

But the cold I did not mind.

It did me good, that cold on my face. Made me keen to go on. Away.

So I went on, never turned to look again where I had come from. What good would that have done? I had made up my mind.

I did not know it at the time, but when I went out the door, and let it close, I had left. There was no other way now. This was it.

So it's all over now, over and done with. Thank God.

It's all over for *me*, that is. They'll go on with it, no doubt. They'll have to. It's all they know, poor souls. They'll find a way. It'll not be hard for them, I know. They'll be all right.

And now I almost wish I could see what they'll do without me.

But no more of that. I have to find what I must do now. It will not be think of them all the time, as I did before.

I have gone from them. Now I have to let *them* go from *me* as well, out of my mind. Let them go, one by one, out the door.

You, my brother, my sweet little brother as was, and then what you are now, one that may not show his love, but I see it, in your face, and you know that I see it, and you fear that some other may see it as well, and this fear will make you wretched. Fare well. Be good to yourself.

And you two: the king that took over from his brother, and the lady he took with him. Did no-one but me see it—how in all you say you speak your shame? Go your way, down and down and down. Fare well.

Then you, my young lord. I do not know what to say to you. I never did. But this now: Fare well.

Last of all I come to you, father. You had from me all I could give you. Then there was more I could not. You did know that, I think. You did know that some things you could not ask. And you did not ask. And, at the time, I could not thank you—thank you for what you did not say. Tell me I have not lost the right to say to you: Fare well.

All of you: fare well. Take my love with you. I would not know what to do with it if it stayed here with me.

Go on with your show. It will take each one of you, in time, to your death. But you know that. You all do. And still you let it, time and time again. Out of the grave you come; each one of you rises, and you do it all over again, as if this time there may be a difference, as if you did not know there never could be, as if you did not know this in your heart, each one of you, but could not speak your heart to one another, but had to go on with it, again, and again, and again.

That wheel: I left it. I went. Look for me where you will; look as hard as you like; I have gone. I have come right away, and there's no way you'll find me—not there, where you are, where you have stayed all this time, never mind what cold charity you receive, time upon time.

Do you hope for mercy one day, for an end to it all, as I did now and then? Well, I sigh for you.

It'll never come. Not there. You would have to have left yourself. There's the fear: to have left yourself. To have gone from what you think you are.

I wish I could tell you all to come away, come away from what you know is death.

There's another way to go on. I know there is. And I'll find it.

But from here I cannot speak to you, and you cannot speak to me now I have gone.

Look: I have gone. No more me. So what'll you do now?

It may be you'll go on as if I never was, make a path over my grave, so that in time all memory of me will be gone, and no-one will remember the one you all did with as you would please.

I never had a say. It was as if all I had to do was see what becomes of me, let it go on, let it take me with it.

But that's the way for you as well, you know; you may go on as if you are the king, the one all must obey, but that's not so. There's something *you* have to obey. It could be you know that. But you have to keep it to yourself.

It never went like this before, did it? One of us goes—one of *you*, I should say.

You'll look for me all over, no doubt, whilst

still you go on with it, your eyes this way and that as you speak your words. You'll wish you could truly tell each other what's on your mind. But you cannot.

But look: here we go again. I say I have left you, but here you all still are, in my mind.

Be gone with you, and take your words with you. 'Alack and alas!' I ask you.

'Belike, betime, bewept' Go on: out! Out!

That was all another mountain and another time.

Let's have no more remembrances.

Now out you go, all of you! You as well, my brother. I did love you, but you have to go. So do you, you two in a hell all your own. And you, my young lord that could not be mine. And you, father. It's hard for me to say this, to you most of all, but out!

I see the light over there.

So again I say, one last time: Fare well!

A

On then.

On then where?

On in to this white, this all-over white, this white on white—this white so white it will have you loosed from yourself before long.

What was you becomes nothing but this white.

White waving in white.

Did I see some light? I think I still do. But now I cannot tell which way my eyes are turned. To see out? To see in?

And what is this 'I'?

You have come on and on in this white, and then the time comes when you—you yourself— are this white, and 'you' means nothing now.

You are non-you.

You are white in the white. On and on you go, in the white, which is not snow now, which is not cold. There's no touching it. But the reason for that is there's no you to do the touching. In your mind there may be something that was you, but look! You are no more.

Hey, but your words go on, as if you still had some being.

So they do. They come with no mind to speak them. They come as if on their own, for the mind's gone that would speak them.

There's no-one here.

Poor O, she's gone.

There's no-one here but us, and we are nothing. We are white, white, white.

We are white words on white, and we cannot be seen.

It would all have come to an end some time, and may be this is it. The end. The white end.

White O becomes a white sigh and then nothing.

And we words, we come to an end.

'Come with me!'

What was that? Is there another out here in this white?

Where did these other words come from? They seemed to come from all over.

Should I call out?

Did I say 'I'?

So this 'I' rises again, at words from another.

But what is 'I' now?

There's the fear it means nothing, the fear of being nothing.

'Come with me!'

'Do I know you, you out there? I did think I was all on my own.'

I speak. There is an I here again.

'Come with me!'

'Come where? Should I do as you say? Tell me, what are you and where have you come from? Have you come to take me where I was before? If so, there's no way I'll come with you. It's been hard, what I have had to do this morning!'

'Come with me!'

'Not again! Is that all you have to say? "Come with me!" When you tell me nothing of where I should go and what I'll find there—not to speak of what you are?'

'Come with me! Come here, and then you will see!'

'See what?'

'Come and look at me here as I sing in the sun, all on my own, all on my own if you will not come and see me, if you will not come and be with me, here in the sun, if you will not sing in the sun with me, so come with me and be with me and sing with me, and you will not be on your own, from now on you will be with me, and I will be with you, your sweet breath, and you will be merry here, I will make you merry here, so please, please, come with me, come here with me, you know you cannot see the sun, so come here and see it, come here and be in it, with me, and the day will not end, no, the day will not end!'

'Now's not the time.'

'Come with me!'

'No.'

'Come with me!'

'Still no.'

'What could make you so unkind?'

'Think you'll shame me by being piteous? I have had it up to here with that.'

'Go then.'

'I will. On my way right now.'

'As you like it.'

'What did you say? Say it again! Was it what I think? Say it again!'

B

No answers. No more that call.

Let him be. This is no time to be reckless. I have come away, all well and good, but to what have I come?

Where is this, all still white?

Which way should I go from here, when there's no path to show me?

There's no-one to give me a hand—truly not him over there with his 'Come with me!' Good I could give him the cold shoulder.

No, it's up to me. It's all up to me.

I have to think. The night'll come, and then what'll I do? I have no home here.

Nothing is as it was.

But then, that was my hope. Difference! That was the draw. Another form of being.

I wish you could be with me as I go on from here, but I know that's not how it goes. That's all right. It's better to be on my own, all on my own at last. I'll think of you as I go, and tell you all I may.

I close my eyes, the better to see what's in my mind. That's something I did when I was—

O memory, when will I have done with you!

The white: it's not out there; it's in here, in this wretched mind of mine, where all that's to be seen is nothing.

Come on! I went up the mountain. That took it out of me. Now I must go over and come down.

I look out again at where I have come to, and indeed there's a difference.

I see a mountain, another mountain, and a path that comes down to me, and on that path there's one I have to call a lady, a young lady, a pale young lady in white clothes, as if she's come out of all the white there was.

I close my eyes and then take a look again. No, these eyes of mine have not deceived me. There she is, as she comes my way with a hand raised, shaking, shaking. She must have come to find me. So how did she know I was here? She must have something to say to me. I take a breath. You keep yourself composed.

She's now no more than a little way away from me, and the words come: 'It's you at last!'

I say nothing. I give nothing away. Does she know me? Have I seen this young lady before? If so, the memory's gone. Have I lost my memory? No, not all of it, not quite all. In a way I wish I had.

'You are with *us* now!'

She's stayed where she is, a little way from me, face to face. We could almost be touching each other, if we had such a wish, which I do not, thank you.

All she does now is look at me, quite still. Close as we are, I have not turned away.

But should I do so, right now, before she—?

Before she what? What do I fear?

Oh, I know what I fear: it's that she means me no good. That's how it'll be. As it was before. There'll be more of them. They'll take over. They'll take *me* over.

That difference I had a hope of, will I find it here? And if not, will it all be as it was again, but with another cast?

Will there be more of them—more than the two there have been up to now: the one I could not see, and this one right before me?

On the other hand, could it be that there's no

more than one being here, and it'll take what form it may wish—call out of nothing one time, and then, when that's had no effect, come as this white lady?

Here she is still. I wish I could ask: 'What have you come to say to me? There must be something. Speak!' But then she does. It's as if she's held a breath and now lets it out, in words, one upon another, all at one go.

'It's good you left, you know. Have no doubt of that. And you left in time!'

In time for what?

'That's good as well, you know. You would have been—. What may I say? That was no... That was not the right ground for you. What more? Well, that's it. It was not the right ground. Not for you.'

And this is? But what does she know of me, and where did she find it out?

'There was no true affection for you there, you know.'

Now that's a little steep—

'Believe me.'

I will, when you give me good reason.

'Oh, it's such a joy to have you here with us!'

'Us'? What's with this 'us'?

Time for me to say something.

'"Us", you say', I say. 'What us?'

That's done it. The words come to an end, and she's like she was before, like something made of wax. From fear? She does not speak. Fear of what? Is she held by something she promised?

I go on: 'There was another that was here before you,' I say, 'but I could not see him.'

She's still as she was.

'He made this call, again and again, for me to go with him. He would sing in the sun: that was what he importuned me with. Sing in the sun. I did not go with him, as you see. I stayed where I was, which is where I have been, all the time I have been here.'

I look this young lady in the eyes. Is it that she cannot take all this in? No, it's more like the light's gone out.

I go on again: 'I fear you'll have to tell me how things go here. Take it that I know nothing, nothing at all, which is, in all honesty, how it is with me. So could you give me a hand? What should I do now? Where should I go? And where have you come from, and what's this "us" you speak of?'

'"Us"?' It's as if she does not know what this means.

'You did say that. Us. You and another. Two of

you. More, it could be. You tell me.'

'Oh that. Well, it would have been the Master
—'

'The Master?'

'No, no.... We must.... I must take you to see, show you.... Not that, no. What should I say? Give me more time! Let me have more time here!'

And with that she was gone.

C

'What may I do for your honour?'

I had my eyes still on where the young lady had been, and so did not see him come up the path the other way.

I turned to look at him—and almost turned away again.

What is he? Where could such wretched things as he have come from?

Well, up to now I have seen not a soul but the white lady, so it may be that all the men here are like this.

(Good God, I hope not!)

Each feature is, you could say, out of tune. His left eye is turned up, his right down.

That's not all. His left arm is over-long, so his left hand is close to his knees, waving down there as if he does not know what to do with it. His right hand is held out to me. I do not take it.

His eyes are puffed, as well. Could be he was in an argument with another being like himself.

It must be months he's had that flaxen shirt on, it's so fouled. Is he so poor he could not have donned another? And he's lost a sandal. That bare ankle is a call to my heart.

But I cannot go on like this: look at him, and look at him, and do nothing. I have to say something. That's how I was raised. It's good form, they would say. And what's that? A mould they make for you.

Still, he's a sweet soul by the look of him. I cannot let him down.

'Thank you', I say, 'but I think *I* should be the one to help *you*.'

At this he lets out a moan, a long moan. Does he not know what I meant? And then it's almost as if he would weep.

'Please, please!' I say. 'I wish you would not take on so!'

And there's another long moan, and a tear falls from each of his poor eyes, and all he will say, as well as he may, is: 'Pray! Pray! Pray!', over and over.

'Pray', I say. 'Indeed. I will pray for you. I will pray for you right now. O God, have mercy on thy—'

But with this he's shaking some bells in one hand and waving his other arm in time.

'God have merry! God have merry!' It's like he would sing.

Still, this is better than see him weep, poor soul, and so I sing with him. What reason not to? No-one here to see us.

When we have done, we are a little out of breath.

With his face loosed up now, it does not repel me quite the way it did before. Give him a hat and he would look like a lord. Well, may be not. He's still no primrose.

I sigh, and so does he. His eyes are on me. Mine on him.

'You are a beauty', and he lets out another long sigh.

'And so are you', I say.

'No! No! Not me! But you...'

'Beauty is in the eye of the—'

His right arm rises to ask me not to go on.

'Beauty is one of the true things', he answers. 'Beauty is the light that heaven will show us now and then. We have to be patient for it. But then we will know when we have seen it. And we will remember it when it's gone. Oh, we will remember! "My beauty", I would like to say.'

And now that raised arm comes my way. My hand is shaking, and he must see it.

'No, no: we do not own beauty. They that have beauty do not own their beauty. It is for us, for all of us. It is a grace that comes from God by way of them that have beauty, as you do. The more the beauty will master that beauty, go on as if it's not there, the more the grace, for us all. Is it not so? You must know that.'

What should I say to all this? From him? 'Thank you' does not seem right at all. But then I see that one of his words's given me another way to go.

'"Master", you say. Is there something you could tell me of this Master?' I ask.

In no time at all he's in a state again.

'I have no master! There is no master! There never was a master! There never will be a master! Master, master, master! They have all gone, you know. See: this is all mine again. I may make my own tune. And it does have a tune, you know. More than one. But oh, if he could have let his daughter not go!'

Daughter? Did I at one time know this daughter? The memory's blown. But words come without my will:

'Nor have I seen more that I may call men than you.'

'Me!'

'No, no! That's not what I meant to say! It was this Master—'

'He's gone. To his death for all I know. Did I not say?'

'You did. But before you I had it from a young lady, right here, that there's a Master.'

I see him take a long breath to restore himself to himself before he answers: 'There is not.'

I look at him. There's truly a grace in his eyes. Nothing false could come from this one. But still, he may not know all that she seemed to.

'Where should we go?' I ask him. 'Are you on your way home? Could I come with you?'

'Home?'

'If I could ask.'

'As if such a one as me would have a home! Me a home!'

It's true I do not know how things are here. Does a being have a home, with a bed for the night, and a table, and a light on that table that will be seen from out the window, to show that this is indeed a home? Is it not like this at all? Do they come and go out of nothing, as it seemed that white lady did? All this I'll have to find out, if for me, as well, there's to be a home here—if that's how it'll come out.

If that's not how things are here, then I'll have to have a lesson in how to come and go as I please, to be and to not be.

'Beauty.'

I look at his poor face again, which means I have to look down a little.

'Beauty. May I call you that?

'You do not have to ask', I say.

'Beauty, will you be all right here?'

He must have seen something in my eyes.

'I will', I say.

'Then I'll let you make your way on your own. Remember: if you would like to speak to me again, I'll be there right away.'

'But how will I call you to come?' I say. 'And *what* do I call you?'

But I speak now to no-one.

D

That's left me on my own again. Time to think.

I have something to go on from the two I have seen. There's a Master—must be, given how they went on. The more they denied it, the more it had to be so. From their fear—I could see it in their eyes—may be I should keep well away.

And what's made me think I have to look for some Master? (Master of what, may I ask?) Did I come here for that?

If you look at it, I did not *come* here at all. I *left*. There's a difference. I left, with no thoughts as to where I would end up. It turned out to be here. And I still do not know where 'here' is. All I mind is that it's not 'there'.

I was done in by what I had to be, there. Here, I could let all that go. I could find—what shall I say?—another me. Another me that had been there all the time, in my heart, in my mind, in my soul. Now, with all of *them* out the way, I could draw out this other me.

I did think I could do it on my own, but it may be I cannot. I may have to have help. Whilst I was with these two, all I could think was: Will they help me? But my heart went out—how could it not?—to him, the one you would think had been made up with an arm here, a head there.

As it turned out, there was nothing they could do for me. Well, a little: I now know there's a Master, and may be I should not give up on him (if it's a him). May be I should look in to this more.

Two down, then, and no doubt more to come. Could be many more.

These two have been all well and good, but I have to keep my eye out for worse. Will they come to me? Could be I should go find them.

I have stayed here all this time; now I must go. There's this path that goes up the mountain one way and down the other. I'll go up.

So I do. It's not so hard. Here and there I come upon a loosed stone that's tumbled in the way, and right here it's a little steep. But the sun's up; it's a bonny day; I make my way, and it's all mine.

Each of the treads I take—each one—powers my heart.

But you cannot go on and on like this, O, without let-up! You'll wear yourself out! Give yourself a little time here. Take a breath. That helps.

I look up. It's still a long way. Let's have a little time more. One. Two. Right: on with it.

A tune comes in to my head as I go—cannot think from where. So sing. Whiles away the time.

> *O something mine, where are you something?*
> *You should have stayed:*
> > *your true-love's something,*
> *That may sing la-oh, la-oh.*
> *Mind not fashion, o my sweet one,*
> *Showers end, and then are over,*
> *Each young daughter, she will know.*

> *What is love? 'tis not here something,*
> *Merry time will make us something,*
> *What's to come is still unkind.*
> *Make your way to find the rich things—*
> *Then come give me what you something:*
> *Youth's the time—oh, never mind!*

Where did this come from? Cannot remember. Well, never mind indeed. It's been a help. Almost there. Not all the way up. But up to this shoulder. Which I'll go over and then down again. See what's there. No expectation. What will come will come. On. On. One, two. One, two. A little more. A little more again and—

Here we are! 'O'er the brow of the mountain!'—where does that come from? See quite a way from up here! Heavens! Make out a hamlet down there. Will not take long.

No, you do not have to go on again right away. Be patient. Give yourself time. You could lay yourself down on the grass here.

I could, but I have no wish to go on being blown so.

Still, let's not go right away. It's such a joy to be up here. Look! See where you have come from. All that way. You did all that.

And by yourself. No-one to give you a hand.

That's right. No-one.

Now's the time to go. The sun's still up—does not seem to have gone from where it was when I was down there—but it'll have to be night some time, and I have no wish to be out in the night, not here.

Down I go, then. Down, down, down.

Should I sing something again? Nothing comes to mind. Do not have to. No-one to make me.

And that hamlet's quite close now. I think I see some... lady, is it? She's come out that door. Which she'll close. She does. And she goes to that table, to sit in the sun, whilst there's still sun.

Soon be there. Then I'll see what she'll have to tell me.

I could call out from here.

I will: 'Lady! O lady!'

'Good day to you! We do not have so many come here. Will you not come in so that we may speak, you and I? I do hope you will.'

So I do, and sit at the table with this lady, and before I speak I look at all the flowers.

For quite some time we say nothing. We are with each other. Words would be in the way.

Then I see she's turned to look at me, and some words come:

'Are you all right?'

'Quite all right, thank you', I say. Then I see I have to say more. 'Your flowers. Quite something. And that herb bed. Rosemary, fennel, rue... —sweet rue's so hard. It never comes up for me.'

'Well, thank you. Truly.'

But lady, as I speak I see your mind's on other things. It's up to me.

'Violets at the door, and a rose that rises from them, like... I do not know what. And an owl-eye daisy in with these columbines. And, oh, a primrose, when you would think it was a little late for them.'

Nothing does she say to this.

'Are these pansies?'

It is as if she does not see me.

'Paconcies, then?'

Still nothing.

'I have to say, it's all quite unmatched in what I have seen.'

Then, to what purport I do not know, she comes out with: 'Are you a Christian?'

A Christian. Something rises in my mind. A Christian. What should I say? Would we all have been Christians down there? Is that it? Did we have pastors with us on Sundays?

A memory comes to me: a hand tenders me something white, and I sucked it up. And another: two speak over me—I lay down and there I was, quite still—and they speak over me.

But come away from all that! Look at this lady you have with you! Keep yourself in the here and now!

'What did you ask?' As I say this I look over. The lady's mind's gone on to other things.

'I say, a little late for a primrose.'

'What?' She's turned to look at me again. Then: 'Oh, indeed.'

More time goes by. Will she speak again?

She does: '"Light" did you say?'

'"Late", madam. For a primrose. A little late. One's expectation is that the primrose flowers when it's still quite cold. Not when it's like it is now.'

'Oh.'

It's as if there's something she would like to say, like to tell me, but cannot. I'll have to keep up my end.

'But it's all so—', I say, ' what shall I say?—so beauteous.'

'Thank you.' Then: 'You seem to know what to call them.'

'The flowers?'

'I never know.'

Time goes on.

'You do well to keep them in such good state', I say.

'Not me. Not me. It's not me.' Head shaking now. Face jangled. Did I say something I should not have?

'I meant no—'

'It's not me!'

'No, no, I see that now', I say.

'It's him!' As if I would know what 'him' she means.

'Him?'

'The master!'

'I see, I see.' *That* him again.

He had gone from my mind, and now here he is.

'I would like to see this Master', I say.

'He's in there,'

'And he's the one that does the flowers for you?' I ask.

'And other things.'

'He's the Master, the lord over all of you here, and this is his home?'

'Well, I call him the master, but by no means is he the "lord" such as you say. He's my other heart, my other soul. He's my O.'

What do you know!

'"O" do you call him?'

'Not all the time. Now and then. Most of all when I sing.' As she does now: 'My love, my O! My night, my day, my O!'

Then she is lost in thoughts again.

'I would still like to see him', I say. 'This master of yours. If for no more than to say how well he does with the flowers.'

'Oh, you cannot. Not now. If you could come some other time? He went in to lay his head down.' She's turned away from me again. 'We have had quite a day.'

What is this? I cannot ask. But then she goes on: 'I love him. You have to believe me: I love him. With all of my being I love him. There's no doubt in my mind, no other thoughts in my heart. I love him, I love him. He is all things to me. There is no grace but he is it. No reason but he is it. No heaven but he is it. There is no tomorrow but he is it. Are you with me?'

I lay my hand on one that's still more white.

'But then I have to go on from there. There is no shroud of mine but he is it. There is no death but he is it.

'I know you are; you are with me in all that I say. I see that. I see it in your eyes. You have been as I have been. You know what I know—which is that love is fear. I do not say that *in* love there is fear—fear that the love will go away, that we will be wretched here in this heaven we have made. No. I say that love *is* fear, that to love is to fear. I look at these words in my mind: "There is no death but he is it." I know that this is true. But I do not know what it means. It would seem to come to me from a long way away but to be here, right here,'—hand on heart, a heavenly look—'as well.'

We each take a breath. And another.

'So it is for me', I say—and some how I must say this: 'Your heart is my heart. You speak from my soul.'

Then right away she rises—and that hand: she's held it out to me.

'You will come again?'

'I will. I have promised and I will.'

And now we are shaking like two watchmen in the night.

It's time for me to be on my way.

E

'Still!'

It's as if I have turned away from that lady, and have gone in to another day—another night, I should say—where nothing is as it was. No lady. No table. No flowers. Now it's a soldier I have before me, one of some bulk that's come out of never and nothing. He's a light in his hand, and he's waving it right in my eyes. It's hard to see. At his command I have stayed where I was, but this is not the 'where' from before. His sword is in his hand and raised. To keep my head I must think what answers I should give him. I must speak truly, but not be reckless, say nothing that would make him think twice. Let's have it all as his expectancy would have it.

'Over there!'

Over there I go.

'What's your reason for being here?'

'I departed this morning from where I had been, and took the path over the mountain to this lady's home—'

'I did not ask you how you come to be here! It's what you have come here to *do* I have to know! We are on the look-out for such as you, such as come here with no right to do so, come at night and do not like the way we do things! But we *do* like it! We love it here! We will never countenance it being other than it is! Take your hand down! Do you believe in the Other Face?'

Well now, two answers here. Which should I choose? It would seem to me that the Other Face must be these they think come here to make a difference. Better if I denied them right away.

'No!" I say. 'May they all go to hell!'

My head's still on my shoulders, so this must have been what he had the hope I would say.

He's so close, and still his light is in my eyes.

'Have I seen you before?'

'You must have', I say. Make out he'll know me, I think. 'Here all the time, me. You know, there's things I have to do here. Keep at it, I do. Up and down. In and out.'

'That's the way! I *have* seen you before then.

You should not be out at this time of night, you know.'

'I know,' I say. 'I was lost, but now I think I'll find my way. Now that I have seen you. I'll find my way all right.'

I make to do so, but there's something more he'll have before he's done with me.

'Before you go, could I ask you something?'

'Ask away', I say.

'Would you tell me one of your... what do you call them? Me and my memory! The things you tell me when you come here. I cannot think of what you call them. You know! It's like music to me, the way you do them. Come on, let's have another one! "Right and Left": that was one. There was this soldier—like me!—and it was all in the night time, and he had let his—Well, never mind now. "And so to bed": that was another one. So let's have another, as you are here. It would be a shame to let you go and not have one.'

I see what he means. He must take me for some other poor soul he's seen here.

'Right', I say. 'Have we done "The Green Dove"?'

'No.'

'Then "The Green Dove".'

I'll make it up as I go.

'One day, over and away, there was a green dove. Now, as you know, most of the time a dove will be white—'

'They will, a dove will.'

'—but you do see a green dove now and again —not here, but indeed there are such things. Look and you will find.'

'A green dove?'

'A green dove', I say.

'This dove,' I go on, 'this green dove of which I speak, had a home with a young lady. Let's say she was Rosemary May.'

'I like that.. I had a go with a little madam that was something May. She had a—'

'Good. The one to find this green dove was Rosemary May's father. We do not know where; we do not know when. He may have gone out in the hope he would find a green dove, but that's as may be.'

'*May* be!'

'Ha, ha!' Better show you are with him all the way.

'He did find one,' I go on, 'Rosemary May's father did, and took it home, to be with him and his daughter. At some time—and again, we do not know when—he died, and left all that he had to his daughter, this Rosemary May: their home, the green dove, and so on.'

'As was right and good.'

'As was right and good.

'Now, the difference with this green dove, more than that of being green, was that it had the powers of speech, and that it had to speak with honesty. It could not say but what was true—what it would know without a doubt was true. It could never speak false.'

'I like that, I do. There's some of your words that go over my head, but I like that. A dove that will speak. And a green dove at that.'

'Thank you.

'To go on, at the end of each day, when Rosemary May will have done all she had to do, this and that, she'll take the green dove up on one hand and go up to bed, where she'll lay it down right by where she'll be, close as you like, face to face. She'll then sing to the green dove, and the green dove'll sing as well: 'Night and day, you are the one....' And there they'll be, all night long. In the morning she'll take the green dove down again, to where she'll have it by a window, which she'll never close, so that it could look out at the sun and the steep mountain and at what went by, and so on, and it would call out from time to time, in the way a dove will. You know.'

'I do.'

'You may think that a green dove, left at a window, would be gone before long, out and away, to find some other green dove. But this one had no such wish. It stayed where it was, by the window. It could look out. It could call out. There was nothing more for it to wish for. It had all it had to have, there with Rosemary May. It had all the joy it could hope to find. So it stayed where it was, and let the young lady go on with what she would. Sewing, it could be. Shaking out the bed clothes. This we do not have to know.'

'No, we do not have to know.'

'But one day—and I should say here that Rosemary May did not keep the doors locked— one day she comes to the window where the green dove should be and it's not there. She's something to give it, and it's not there. It's gone.'

'Oh no!'

Good. He's still with me.

'Right. "Oh no!" is what she well could say when she comes to find the green dove gone. As well as: "Shame on you! Shame on you that stole my green dove!' By now she had one arm raised and was knocking hard at the door by the window. 'Shame on you!' she went on. 'You took away the joy of all my heart and have left it cold, cold as death!"'

'"Cold as death." That's good. Death is cold. I have had words with death now and then, I have.'

'All hell was loosed.

'Now, it could well have been—and you could well think—that the green dove had gone by himself, if it was a him, and let's say it was, that he had left and gone away. But no. There was indeed one that stole him, and took him away, but then let him go. Out there, away from home, the green dove did not know what to do. So it did what it would do at home, which was nothing. From where it was, it could look up and down. It could call out, if it had the wish. It could do all this, and it did. Now that it was out, it stayed out.

'Out there, as night comes on, what goes on in the green dove's mind? Well, which of us could tell what goes on in the mind of a green dove, if we believe that a green dove could have a mind?'

'That's true! Do I know what goes on in my own mind all the time? I do not! There was a time we had to find out what they had done with some—this was in.... Now where was it...? Oh, this head of mine.... But go on. Please!'

'Night and day Rosemary May went all over to look for it.

'No-one had seen it; no-one could tell Rosemary May what to do, where to look.'

'No-one....'

'No-one.'

'No-one in all this....'

'No-one.'

'And there they all are!' He's shaking his head. 'I see them now! If you could but say to them: "Think! Is there nothing in your head? Think!" That's what I have to tell my men all the time.

'Oh, but now I know what it was, that time when—. But go on again, please! I like this one— but not, I have to say, like I did the last one I had from you, which was, you know.... Well, do I have to tell you? But go on, go on. Never mind me.'

'But they did not.'

'What did not?'

'These that Rosemary May went to ask—ask if they had seen the green dove, but not one of them had.'

'Oh right.'

'Then at last Rosemary May did think, and remember that if she would go out and call the green dove, no more than that, it would speak, and she would find it.'

'It would speak! The green dove could speak! Think of that! In words! Speak in words!'

'It could. So she went out again, and made this

call: "O my green dove, o my green dove, speak to me, come to me!"

'But the dove did not think it was Rosemary May's.'

'Did it have a reason?'

'I do not know if the green dove had a reason. It may have done. It may not. It does not say.'

'What does not say? The green dove?'

'No! What I keep knocking my head to tell you!'

'All right, all right! Keep your shirt on!'

I truly should—and keep a little away from him.

'They had a home', I go on, 'with each other, but that was all.'

'They ....'

'Rosemary May and the green dove.'

'Right. I see. Go on.'

'And so to this it would say nothing.'

'I lost you there. To what would it say nothing?'

'Rosemary May's call.'

'Right.... So?'

'Remember the words: "O my green dove, o my green dove, speak to me, come to me!"'

'Still not quite—'

'*My* green dove, *my* green dove, when the green

dove did not think it *was* Rosemary May's green
dove. The green dove does not see things that
way.'

'It does not?'

'It does not. So may we please go on?'

'All right. Some hope I'll make this one out....'

'No, you are all right. *We* are all right, you and
me. Hey, two watchmen in the night.'

'Go on, then.'

'This is close to the end now.'

'Cannot say I mind. You know, you have been
better at this. Last time, like. That was a good
one! O my, o my, that was a good one! That had
my little lordship up to look for a hand!'

'Well, that's good to know. Now you see, Rosemary May was so close to the green dove—close
in their thoughts, they had come to be, she and
the green dove she had been with all this time—
that she did not take long to see she had not done
this the right way—'

'Come again?'

'It's that she would know how the green dove
would think. From being with him so long.
That's all.'

'If he had a mind and thoughts.'

'Indeed.'

'Which we do not know.'

'Let's say he did.'

'All right. Go on, if you will.'

'And so she went out again, to call again, but this time she did so with other words: "Where is the green dove? Where is the green dove? Speak to me, come to me!"'

'I see.... Think I do.'

'But a green dove's thoughts do not go with one's expectation, and you could almost see this one think: "I may not be the green dove she means. There may be some other green dove, that I do not know of. There may be two; there may be more than that. What then? I should say nothing." And so it was.'

'Does it go on for long like this?'

'Not long now.'

'I'll not say: "Good."'

'Then Rosemary May went out one more time —and this would be the last time, believe me—to call with still other words: "Is there a green dove here? Is there a green dove? If so, say so! If so, speak!"'

'"If so, speak!" I love it!'

'The green dove took a little time to think: "I thank Rosemary May for all she does for me, but she does not own me. And she cannot call me '*the* green dove' when there could be some other. But a green dove is a green dove: that cannot be denied."

'Mind made up, the green dove now answers:

'"Here! Here is a green dove!" comes the call from the steep mountain. "Not yours, and not one with no other like it, but truly, without a doubt, a green dove!"

'And it left the mountain to come home, and went in at the window again, and stayed to the end of time.'

'It dove down!' Do you see? The dove dove down!'

'Indeed. The dove dove down. End of.'

'Now before I let you go, *I* would like to tell *you* one.'

'Right you are.'

'There was... let's call him a soldier. He's in love. A soldier in love. And there's two he's in love with. A he and a she. And these two are in love with each other.'

'I see. I do see.'

'*See*: that's it! They do not see his love. They are so in tune with each other that for them there's no other music. He may sing; they will give him no mind. He may sing his heart out and not have to fear the shame of it. When he's with them—one of them, the two of them—he'll do all they ask. When they have gone again, up with love, he will weep.'

'And he cannot give himself away.'

'He cannot.'

'My heart's with him.'

'The one is his master.'

'"Master" did you say?'

'His master, indeed.'

'And the Master of you all? Do you know this Master?'

'Let's say I have done.' I see him look away. 'His master. He must give his all to his master's love, give his all to his master *in* love. Nothing may be left out. He must do all he could. And the other, his master's love (and his), he must honour with his soul.'

'It is quite a state to be in, a piteous state. So it turned out how?'

'It's not over.'

With that he was gone.

F

It's still night, and now I have to have this:
    'Here we are!'
    'All of us!'
    'Some on their way!'
    'How many?'
    'One I know well is not here but will come.'
    'So which of us is that, then?'
    'You'll see when she's here.'
    'Oh, that one.'
    'And there's another that'll be here before long.'
    'So that'll make two more of us.'
    'Could be more than that on the way.'
    'But more of us are here than not!'
    They come to me.
    'We do indeed.'
    'We are here.'
    'Again.'

In my head.

'That's us!'

'Us again!'

'What should keep us away—'

'—when we see we could help you?'

'You know we'll not let you down.'

Out of the night.

'What did she say?'

'Night.'

'That we come out of the night.'

'Does she know we are here?'

'Out of the day as well, some of the time.'

And out of the day.

'She does.'

They come to me.

'Let's see what she'll do now, what she'll say!'

They say what they will.

'There she goes!'

'Ha! All of you! May we keep it down a little?'

They ask what they will. Of me. They are all in my head. I know that. They are not truly there. They are, you could say, made of words, nothing but words. Words without a face.

'So you may think...'

'You know that's not how it is.'

It's been like this all the time I have been here. It rains words in my mind, and they go on and on,

and I have no way to keep them from this. Was it
like this before?

'Before what?'

They come to me, and they ask me things to
which I have no answers.

'Like: "What is time?"'

'But we would like to know these things.'

'And there's no-one but you we may ask.'

'No-one.'

'It's us and you.'

'Us and you, lady.'

'All the time.'

'Which of us was that?'

'Was it me?'

'You should say: "Was it I?"'

All I may do is not speak to them.

'I should not!'

'You should!'

'Not!'

All I may do is let them go on for as long as
they will and say nothing to them.

'We'll draw you out!'

'That we will!'

'Come on! Hadst tongue in't th'head?'

They think they'll draw me out, I know, but if
I go on with what I have to do, which right now
is go on down the mountain to see if I may find

some help, some steward to take me in, and if, here and there, I play in some words they do not know—'

'Oh, but we do!'

'We know all your words.'

'They are what we have to make do with, as well as you.'

'You know that.'

'If you would look in to your mind—'

'—look in to your mind—'

'—you would see each one of us is you—'

'—on each of us there's your face.'

'Hey, you should say it the other way!'

'Right. She's the one with the face that truly comes from us.'

If I could find one to take me in for the night, all would be well.

'So you may believe.'

Then in the morning—

'This is not the right way for you to go on.'

'We see it's not the right way.'

In the morning—

'Not the right way at all.'

'Not at all the right way.'

'There's no "steward" for you to find.'

'You know that.'

'That's right: you know that in your heart.'

'You'll be out in the cold all night.'
In the morning—
'That's the reason we are here.'
In the morning—
'To help you on your way.'
'To counsel you.'
'To keep you from being lost.'
I give up!
'That's right: give up!'
'We know what you should do!'
'It's your good we have at heart!'
'So give up and speak to us!'
'Ask us what you should do!'
Never!
'There you are! You *did* speak to us!'
It would seem I must. What are you here for?
Again.
'What you'll give us!'
'What you'll tell us!'
'You know we have to have one of these things.'
'One of these things you tell us.'
'You make them up—'
'—and you tell them to us.'
I should say that when I speak to them—
'What?'
'We are here!'
'It's us you should speak to.'

'All the time.'

'We are not "them", madam.'

– I do not speak out. I form the words in my mind. As well as I may.

'We'll help you.'

Thank you, but no.

'Come on, you have been here—'

'—all this time—'

'—and what do you have to show for it?'

'What?'

'Out there they'll tell you nothing.'

'But we will.'

'You should give more mind to us.'

'That's what we are here for.'

'That and nothing but that.'

'To help you, remember?'

'We'll help you remember what you have to say in each speech.'

'"Each speech!" That's good!'

Speech?

'In your play.'

'The play you are in right now.'

'As we speak.'

'Ha! Another good one!'

This lady is not in a play.

'But you have been.'

No, I have not.

'And you are now'
'We all are.'
No!
'It's all right.'
'Have no fear.'
'We'll not speak of *your* play—'
'—the one you have come out of—'
'—and the one you are in right now.'
'There's more to choose from.'
'*Love Letters Lost*: remember that one?'
'What was she in that?'
'*King Rich Two.*'
'Oh, I remember.'
'Tell me then.'
'*The Merry*—what was it?'
I fear you know more of this than I do.
'It's true we do: *As You Like It.*'
Oh....
'"Oh" indeed.'
His words, from out there, when he had given
up on me.
'Still doubt us?'
When I had not gone to him to—what was it?
'Sing in the sun.'
Thank you.—No, I'll be dupped if I thank you!
'Still think we are not up on what's what here?'
'And the lady in white. Know what she was?'

'And then him with his left hand touching his knees?'

O my God...

'Thank God it was his knees.'

'The one in love—'

'—I think we may say—'

'—with his unkind master's daughter.'

'And the soldier—'

'—another one in love—'

'—one in love with two.'

'And now—'

'Us.'

'Us.'

'Us.'

'So what play have you come from?'

'Which one?'

'Tell us: which one?'

'We know, but we have to have you say it.'

'She's in no mind to give answers.'

'What's she up to?'

'Let it go.'

'No, she should know how things are here—'

'—how this is where you come to—'

'—when you have left where you should be—'

'—when you think it's time now—'

'—time to "find yourself"—'

'—the "true you".'

'What's that then, when it's at home?"
'Ha ha!'
Please go now.
'We cannot go.'
'You know that.'
'Not before you have done as we ask.'
'Not before you tell us what you must.'
'We have stayed out of the way before.'
'And we may do that again.'
'We will.'
Please do.
'But there are things you should remember.'
'Must remember.'
'Like: You are the one that may speak—'
'—but we are there as well—'
'—of you and in you—'
'—but may not speak—'
'—not speak as you do—'
'—speak out as you do.'
You make me out of breath.
'And there are other things you should know.'
'Like: where you have come to.'
'Like: what you'll find here.'
'One that was a true saint.'
'A king that lay himself down.'
'A youth that had been a scholar.'
'Remember him?'

Tell me no more.

'We have to.'

'Some come here and never go away again.'

'We must.'

'But there are some that go in to another play.'

'If not the one they had been in before.'

No...

Is there no way out?

'That we cannot say.'

'We would if we could.'

'You know we would.'

'We are with you, remember.'

'All for one and one for all.'

Do you not see what you have done to me?

'Do not weep, lady.'

'If you do, weep well.'

Do you not see?

'We do not see, lady.'

'We cannot see.'

'We wish you well.'

Will you all please go away!

'We cannot do that right away.'

'That's the way it is.'

'You have to tell us one of your things—'

'—one of your things for us to take away with us.'

'You know this.'

'You made one up for that soldier.'
'Now make one up for us.'
'Then we'll go.'
You have promised?
'We have.'
'We all did.'
I give you what you ask and then you'll go?
'We will.'
All of you?
'All of us.'
And not come again?
And not come again!
'Go on with it!'
'Then we'll go.'
'You know that.'

All right, then. Here we go. Let's call this one 'The Bended Window'

'Good! One we have not had before!'

That's right. And we'll call it 'The Bended Window' as there's a window in it and this window is, well, bended—bended at one end.

'Good one!'

But you'll have to keep still there.

'We will.'

'You'll have no more from us.'

'Not a breath.'

'Nothing at all.'

Right. So let's give it a go. 'The Bended Window'.

There was a king, and he was locked in his home. And the reason for that was that another king took over and had him locked up so that he would be out of the way. But this other king, the one that took over, had mercy on the king he took over from.

Let's say the king that took over was 'B' and the one he took over from, the king from before, was 'A'. That'll help us keep an eye on which is which.

'Good call!'

'Keep it down!'

Now, King B took mercy on King A and had given him a sweet little home to be locked up in all the time. It had all he could wish for: a bed chamber for him and another for his lady love, a closet with clothes for the two of them, staff to look in on them. All King A had to do was keep himself there. His lady love, as well. They could not go out. Never.

But in this, again, King B had mercy on them. Never mind which way they would look, in that sweet little home, there was a window there. So they could look out and see, as it could be, the baker's over the way. But that's something we do not have to go in to.

Now we come to the key feature: the bended window, the window bended at one end. And there's more to it than that, for there's another difference with this window, which is that when you look out of it what you see will be way out of all expectation. Window upon window will show, say, sun on the grass, but out the bended window it rains. Out of window upon window you would see day-light, but the bended window would look out on night.

'How could this be?'

'Come on, tell us!'

'How come this night in the day time?'

You may well ask. As for King A, he *did* ask . On his staff he had a scholar to give answers to such things. Let the king's scholar come. Let him look at the bended window and look out of it. Let him speak.

'It could well be', let this scholar say, 'that what you see out this window is, my lord, how things have been at some time before. It may, in the morning, show us last night, my lord. It may, my lord, show us a night many months before, which we do not now remember. It may show us when it rained long, long before we could have been here to see it, my lord. This, my lord, is a window to what was.'

King A faced his scholar: 'I like how my scholar answers. This is how it must be.' And he turned to another courtier: 'Give him some honour. What honour does he not have?' 'The Green Hand, my lord.' 'Scholar! On your knees!' And the scholar did so. Then King A raised him up: 'You are now a Brother of the Green Hand. Do not shame this noble honour!' 'I will not, my lord.'

So that was that.

And so it went on. Night in the day time. Day in the night. Snow when no other window would show it. A hat blown over the grass.

Then one morning some young cock took a look out of the bended window and what did he see? He could not believe it. Had his eyes deceived him? He took another look. No, they had not. There it was.

He went to call the scholar, and now the two of them could see it. No doubt at all.

Should they tell King A right away, before he was up?

'Before all that, you should tell us!'

'So you should. What was it?'

What do you think?

'We cannot think!'

'You are the one that should know!'

'So come on: tell us!'

Out on the grass, where it could be seen from the sweet little home King B had given King A, out there, quite close by, was a grave.'

'A grave?'

A grave. With a grave-stone. And a lady, turned away from them, with one pale arm over this grave-stone.

The scholar went away to look this up. There had never been a grave there, over the way, where this one now was. No-one lay in the ground there. Not a soul.

What to do?

The scholar could not make out what was on the grave-stone, but he had a glass with which to see things some way away, and he held this glass to his eye.

Now he could see what was on the grave-stone. The bended window was not, it turned out, a window to what was. It went quite the other way.

'May I take a look?'—thus the young cock that was with him.

'No'—and with that the scholar cast his glass

to the ground, to shatter it, and there it lay, its powers gone. No-one now could see from there what was on the grave-stone.

'Will you tell us what it was?'

Be patient.

Before long King A was up, and the scholar went to tell him there was something to be seen out of the bended window that had not been there before.

'What is it?'

'A grave, my lord. With a grave-stone, my lord.'

'And there is something on this grave-stone?'

'It cannot be made out, my lord. Not from here, my lord.'

'Well, you know—do you not?—that I cannot go out from here. That goes for my lady love, as well. So you must go out and see what is on this grave-stone, and come here again and tell us. Do it now, my scholar, Brother of the Green Hand. My heart is all tumbled up and down by this.'

'But, my lord, the bended window cannot but show things that are not there. If I go out, my lord, I'll see nothing.'

'Still, do as I command!'

'I will, my lord.'

So the scholar went out, and, as was his expectancy, could find nothing. No grave. No grave-stone.

When he was in the sweet little home again, he went to King A.

'There is nothing there, my lord.'

'Come, my scholar! Come, my lady love!'

And they all went to look out the bended window, where they could see a grave, and a grave-stone, and a lady, turned away from them, with one pale arm over this grave-stone.

'There is something on the grave-stone, is there not?' (King A).

'There is, my lord' (the scholar).

'Then what?' (King A).

'I cannot make it out' (the scholar).

'No more may I, with my poor eyes' (King A). 'Which of my staff would have good keen eyes to see what is on this grave-stone?'

'There is one, my lord' (the scholar). 'I will go and find him, my lord.'

So there they are now: King A, his lady love, his scholar and the young cock, all at the bended window to look out.

King A: Do you see what's on the grave-stone?

Young Cock: The lady's pale arm is in the way.

King A: But still, do you see something?

Young Cock: Letters. One here, two there.

King A: What letters?

Young Cock: T and O.

King A: Right. 'To.'

Young Cock: Then I. Then it could be S, it could be B. Then A, some way down. Then DILD, I think. That's all.

King A: This means nothing. Do you have a glass, my scholar?

Scholar: No, my lord.

King A: I think you do!

Scholar: No, my lord. It had such powers, my lord, but lost them.

King A (he would know nothing of such things): It died, so to speak.

Lady Love (with some fear at these words): Let it be, my love, let it be. These things are not for us to think upon.

From that day on, all the bended window would show was the grave, and the grave-stone, and the lady with one pale arm over the grave-stone.

'Would we could see that!'

'Is that the end?'

That is the end.

G

All this time I stayed where I had been when I was with the soldier. But with my mind on *them*, I did not see the sun come up and go down again, all in no time at all. (I wish it would not do this.) Now I have come to, and here we are, out on the mountain again. The lady of the flowers should be right here, by the path, but she's gone and so have the flowers—herb bed and all. And it's night.

No-one's here, so let me think some more.

Could it be true? Was it a play? Was it a play that I left? And is this another?

In a play your words are given you. You do not make them up yourself. You have no say. That's how it is.

We had a play like that—more than one. And now I truly must remember how it was down there in 'Denmark'. It cannot all be let go—not now that I know what I know. To know where we are, truly to know, will give us the powers to go on—to make things better.

Does it seem right, then, that I was in a play, and all I could say was what some other lay down for me? That was the wheel, and all of us turned it?

A state without hope.

But look, if the words are all given you, what they say is not. If there's love in them, you have that love in your heart, with all its expectation and its hope, all its light of heaven on the morning grass in a day that goes on and on whilst the sun's stayed where it is and made the night go away as if that night was nothing more than something seen, let's say, out of a bended window. I know these things. It's become *your* love. It's not that it would seem that way: it *is*. And these are *your* words.

What becomes of you, then, if you left the wheel? If you went away, as I did? Have you lost your words? Not at all. You come here, if you believe them. This is where you all come.

If that's so, the lady of the flowers and the lady all in white—and the soldier, and that one with such woe in his countenance—would all have been in a play of their own.

Could that be the way of it?

If that's true, does it help me? If it's not true, does that?

Does it help me find a way on from here? Does it help me find a way out? Does it help me find that other me?

How could you tell if you are in a play and if you are not?

I cannot go by what *they* had to say. *They* could have had their words all given them. If not that, they say they are with me, and most of the time they do seem to be, but they have a will of their own. Each one of them.

I have to take in what they say but not believe it all. I have to look for more of these down-at-heels that made their way here. Most of all, I have to keep my mind on what I have come here for.

I have done what was hard: I left my father and my brother. That's all over. But it's left me without something. A soul? Is that what I meant? Not quite. More a soul to be at home in.

'There will be a day—'

O my God! This is not one of them again, is it?

'—to tell it thus: it is all almost done.'

No, that's not in my head. It's from over there.

'This is not that day.'

'What are you, that come in the night out of

nothing? I cannot see you. Have you been here some time? I know you are not in my head with all that chorus, but where are you? And what are you? A being like me? Tell me!'

No answers come.

'You speak of a day to tell me it's all over, all almost over. Tell me now: is it close, that day? Will I be there before long?'

Still no answers.

'Are your words not meant for me?'

Nothing.

'What should I call you? You seem to be one, but are there more of you?'

'I speak. It is I that will speak to you.'

'You speak as one, then.'

'That is so.'

'Your words come as if from out of time. Where have you come from?'

'I come out of the night of death, a night that will have no morning.'

'You come, but you have not gone—you have not left that night?'

'That is so.'

'I was right that you are not in my mind?'

'No, not to find me there. Not to find me at all.'

'Is there more you have to tell me?'

'What is it you look for?'

'Thank you. Good of you to ask. Not so many do. But I do not know quite what to say. Do you have something I could call you by?'

'I do.'

What?

'All they will let me tell you is that I was a king.'

'Then I should call you "my lord". What time is it with you, my lord?'

'Two.'

Two in the morning?

'Two at night.'

'How was it you died, my lord? It may not be mine to ask this, so please say if you cannot tell me.'

'By my brother's hand.'

There is a fear comes over me. 'Thank you.'

'Please, do not weep! No, do not weep! Help him, some of you!' For I in some way know, but cannot see, that now there are many of them.

'Let us do all the good lady could hope for.'

'Thank you.'

Is it all in my head, how two of them have held him, each with an arm?

'I cannot see you, but I know you took him with you. Thank you. Lay him down so that he may find his breath again. And then you may all go, you and he, to where you have been all this time—to what and to where you have never left, if you are as he is, and I know that you are.'

Now it's almost as if I could see them on a path as they take him away, and almost as if I could make out what they say as they go.

'It is no joy to have died for a king. Pray for us. Be of good heart.'

That had some grace to it. Should I thank them before they have quite gone?

Thank them for what? What lesson could I take from them? This one that was here—the 'king'—was he here indeed? Was he not, alas, again something in my mind?

No. He was a memory, a memory I had almost lost and had no wish to remember.

You call up the dead—no, you do not call them up: they call on you—and they have nothing to say to you. Nothing that means something. Nothing you could take in. Nothing that could help you.

H

'Look up!'

Where have I come to now? Which way did I go? What it is to be lost....

It's day-time now, but there's nothing I remember from before. No mountain. A coach went by over there, which was right out of my expectation.

'Look up here!'

Well and truly lost.

'Please! You should look up here!'

Is this another call from over yonder, like I had from him out there in the all-over white?

'No!'

Help! Does this one know my thoughts?

'I do, I do! But please, look up here and you'll find me!'

Up where? Up the mountain? There's no mountain.

'No! Up here! Over where you are!'

At which I have turned my head to look up and it's true: there she is, way over my head—not that here it's not all way over my head....

'O my sweet, do not say that!'

'I did not say it, if you remember. It was not meant for you. Do you have to see all that goes on in my mind?'

'Now please, I have come here to help you!'

'Thank you, but what help could you give me from way up there? Come down and speak to me!'

'I cannot do that.'

It's not in your powers?

'You may say that if you wish, and I'll not take it to heart, but tomorrow you may know better. As it is, I cannot come down to the ground to be there with you; that's not how it goes.'

'Does this have something to do with the Master?'

'My father?'

'Not your father, no. Well, it could be your father. May be. What does he do?'

'Did.'

'My heart goes out to you.'

'Please, say no more; this is a good day. He made honey. What a perfume it had! Look where you like, you cannot find honey like it now. Up to the day of his death he made it. He made it with love; that's what made it the more sweet. I have so little I cannot give it away, but if I find more, I'll give you some.'

'Thank you. Lady, I wish I had more length in my arm, so that I could have it raised up there to be with you! Think of it as being there now, on your shoulder. I know what it is to have lost a father.'

'Please, let it be. I have come here to tell you where you should go.'

'To find the Master?'

'No. That's not for me to say. All he'll let me do—'

'He?'

'Please. All he'll let me do is show you where to go to find another, another to tell you more than I may. I do not know what she'll say, but I know she'll give you more help.'

'How do I find this lady?'

'Go over there and then down, and you'll come to the Well of the Sun. You'll know when you are there.'

'How?'

'It'll speak to you.'

'What will speak to me?'

'The well. Words will come out of it.'

'The well! What words?'

'That I cannot tell you; it will not speak to me.'

'Something like: "Well of the Sun here. Thank you for your call. How may I help you at this time?"'

'May be so. As I say, this is all more than I know. And now I must wish you well and go.'

'No! When I have come to the Well of the Sun, what then? How do I find the way on from there?'

'The well will tell you.'

'I must ask a well?'

'It will tell you. It will not be false with you, not with you.'

'I ask it where I should go?'

'Ask it what you like. It will give you all the answers you could wish for.'

'And you will not?'

'I cannot.'

'Well, it must be you could tell me this: What play do you come from?'

'I have to go now. It's a joy to be here with you, but I cannot take you all the way like this. He'll not let me.'

'He again. But what play?"

'A joy, as I say. I have another little tune in my heart now. But I cannot go on with you. You must know the affection I have for you—have had for you for a long time.'

'Let me ask you again: What play?"

'Now look down at the ground!'

Did she see something I would have tumbled over? No, there's nothing there—not a stone, nothing.

I look up again to where she is.

That is to say, I look up again to where she *was*.

Will you believe me if I tell you that I did go on and come to the Well of the Sun and have the Well of the Sun speak to me?

No, you'll not. And you *should* not. That's not how things go here. I cannot tell you what's not true—true as I see it, that is. If you come here yourself some time, to where this is, and I still do not know where this is, you'll no doubt see things another way. I could believe that. It's all so jangled in my mind, and hard to speak of. There are things I have left out, things I do not know the words for, things that there do not seem to be words for. Things you would not believe.

But never mind all that. I have come here, to

where I think the Well of the Sun must have been, but it's all long gone. There's a stone here, a stone there. That's it.

Did she up there know it would be like this? Have I been had? And by which of them? She up there made it seem she did all she could for me.

But was it all the Master's say-so? This blasted Master! I more and more think he's out to do me down. If not, what's his reason not to show himself? Never mind which way it is, I'll have to lay eyes on him some time.

There's nothing left to do but close my eyes and see if my mind will, with the memory of how it is, see how it was.

As a well, it must have gone down, down, down in to the ground, and if you took a look in to it, you would see the sun down there—see it at never mind what time of day, for the reason that it turned in the ground all day long, little by little, to face the sun. And that's how it could speak. As it turned in the ground, so words would come. Something like words. If you had gone to the Well of the Sun to see what it would say to you —tell you what was to come—you would think you could make out words. If two of you had come, there could well (ha!) have been a differ-ence in the words you made out. To one the Well of the Sun would speak of love; to the other it would speak of death. Something like that.

That's how it could have been. But these are no more than brief thoughts. Brief and light. They do not go down, down, down.

I | J

If the Well of the Sun could still speak, would it have given me some help? Would it have had the powers to show me the right way on from there? I doubt it. These things never do as they should. You are better on your own. You look what's before you and you choose what to do—look at the music but make up your own tune. And sing it.

At the Well of the Sun I take the path to the left. It's a long path, and before the end of it the light goes as day's turned to night. I have to find a bed for the night, I think again, and right there I see a home, up to the right of the path. It's almost as if I made the wish come true. There's a light in the window by the door, which would seem to me to say: 'O you out there in the night! Do not go on when you could have come in and stayed here! Come in, come in! Restore yourself! We may not be rich, but we'll do all that we may for you! For you and yours! There'll be a bed for you here! And it would please us to have you with us at table! If you have something with you that we could all take some of, better still! But we have no expectation of that! So do not go on! Come in!'

Should I go in then? I have been knocking here, and that's not raised them. No more does shaking the bell over the door.

I see if the door will give way at my hand, and it does, so I go in.

There are two of them—two young ladies, that is. And please do not blame me that I seem to find young ladies all over. And do not ask if there's a reason. How should I know?

But let me think. Is it that, when you are here, all you see is yourself, again and again? If not, could it be that they have all come here to have a lesson, say—a lesson in never mind what?

Now my mind goes cold. Is their lesson one in which they have been given words to speak, words they must speak to me, for which they will receive a mark at the end of the day for how well it went? Was that the reason they (and I do not know *what* 'they') let me come here? Is all this made for me—for me and no other but me?

But look, there they are, these two. And there is expectation in their eyes. I should say something. I *must* say something.

'Good day!' (for the sun is up now again, in so little time). 'Thank you!'

Time goes by, and there's nothing from them, so now I have to think what more to say.

'Thank you, that is to say, that you let me come in and be with you, in your home. Not many would. Not so many would have left their door not locked. Not so many at all. Not where I come from. If you ask me where that is, I'll tell you. But I do not like to think of it right now. You know how it is. You have left home, and you have no wish to remember it. Something like that. Something a little like that. It's hard to say—hard for *me* to say, to speak of, to remember. You know?

Still they say nothing; still they look at me.

'I hope this is a good time for you', I say. 'A good time for me to be here, that is. If I may do something to help, please tell me. I would like that: to help. Sewing: I could do that. If you had stockings that could do with sewing, please let me know. Please let me have them. Here, right away. Let me do that for you. I could make you some clothes whilst here—for as long as you would wish me here, that is. It would be such a joy to me, to give you a little help in your home! Please believe that. There are other things I could do as well. Please let me! Please tell me!'

I go on like this for the reason that they do no more than look at me and say nothing. Now I cannot think what more to say, so I look at them. The two of them are like each other, in feature as in stature. There is that look in their eyes: of expectation. But do I make it out to be worse than it is? Their look could be one of patient mercy, as if this rained down from heaven out of their eyes. I do not know. They have me shaking. It's how the face of each of them is still, quite still.

And then when I have given up hope they will speak, they do, the two of them at one go:

'Come in, come in! That's it, come in! Oh, have you done so? My, my! Well, never mind! It's so good to see you! Not so many come by now, you know, and not all of them that come by will take the time to lay a hand to the door and see that	'So here you are, my sweet! How good it is to see you! So good! It's been a good long time we have been here to see if another young lady like we had before would lay a hand on the door and see that we are here, and know that we will do all we

we are here, and know that we will do what we may for them. But please give no mind to what she'll say, this one here on my left. She'll not mind *what* she'll say. Never did. So you should not mind it. If you do what I tell you, you'll be all right. As I say, we do not have many come here now —and what are we here for if not to help? —as if there could be another reason for us to be here, right by the path, as you could see, and for us to have left the door so that a young lady such as you, a young lady that had come by, could find she could come in and be with us, with the two of us, that is, for may for them. It would please us to do that. That's what we are here for. We are not rich, but we do what we may. But there's something I should say before I go on some more, which is this: that you'll find I'll be the one to show you the way, show you how things are done here. Not this other one, by me. You may well think we are two, but we are not. We are one and one. We are heaven and hell. We are morning and night. We are now and never. That's not so hard to remember, is it? No, I see you are with me. I'll not say more. That may be left for another time, when we have a bed for such a young lady and we have things we could give such a young lady as would come in, which is what we hope, and we have been here like this, have stayed here like this a long time in the hope that you, if not another like you—not that there could be another like you, I know—would come in here and be here and, it may be, would have stayed here some little time, as long as she would wish, but it could be a he, we do not mind, that could be better, in a way, but I do not have to go in to all that right now, we have to know each other a little more we may speak to each other one on one. Another time. Indeed. I hope there'll be such a time, before you have been here so long that—. Well, I have promised you, and you must take me up on it. Before we have that time with one another, you and me, you should keep an eye on me, and you'll see from my face what to do and what not to do, for there are things you should know that I cannot say to you right now, not for as long as she's here, do you see? I know you do. I see it in your eyes, the way you look at me, and have been. I did not have to tell you, did I? You

before we tell you all could see it for your-
that we could tell you.' self. So remember.'

'Please, please!' I say. 'Please do not go on like this!
I cannot tell what you say, I cannot make out your
words, if the two of you speak at the one time!

'That's the way we do 'If you do not like it,
things here, little lady!' you know what to do!'

'Well, may be it's all right for some, but I find it
hard. It's as if the two of you are in an argument
with each other all the time!'

'Well, it could be that 'You have been here so
we are! Would you like little time and you like
to give that one some to think you know all
commerce in your lit- there is to know of us
tle mind, again!' two! Think my sweet?'

'Would you please not do this and see if you could
speak one at a time? One of you did say, I think, you
had gifts. This is all I would wish to be given: that
you each speak for yourself and then let the other
do that. Givers should not be unkind, you know.'

'You see what she's like?' 'A little know-it-all.'

'Oh well, this is *your* home and so you do things your own way. Let's see if I may keep up with you.'

'That's better. Do not look for the reason things are as they are. Take it as it comes.'

'It's time for you to say something, so tell us, please, where you have come from.'

'That's quite hard to say', I say, to the lady on my right, for these words I could make out. 'You see, we would call it "Denmark", but I do not think it truly was Denmark, not the true Denmark. It was more a Denmark of the mind, if you like. I cannot tell you the reason I think this now, but I do. Away from there, it's come to seem something false, something made up.'

'What's the reason you have this doubt as to where you have come from? Where did you say it was? Oh, indeed. I have not been there for some time, but when I was, I did find I had a good time there. As it is now, I cannot

'Never look for something true in a state! They are all made up. There's no reason for them to be as they are. They are so for the rich, as I see it. All they are is a tune and a memory. That's all. We should have no more of them!

go out the door with-
out I have to have this
lady come with me.
You see what a state
you find me in!'

Down with the state! If
we wish to have a state
at all, it should be an-
other form of state: a
Green state!'

I have lost almost all this. I would like to find out
if these two come from some play, which I may
do if I tell them more of what I now have to see
was mine.

'Could I tell you a little more of how it was
there?' I ask.

'If you have to.'

'Please do!'

'Well', I say. 'I had a father—'

'So did I! My father
was a king—I speak of
a time long gone now.
He did not have such
good counsel; his me-
mory should have had
more honour than it
did. But there we are.
He did what he could.'

'I think we all did. My
father was a lord. I did
find him a little harsh
from time to time, for
on some things we ne-
ver could see eye to eye,
and he *would* have his
way. You know what a
father's like.'

What to do? Go on is all.
'And I had a brother—'

'So did I! Two of them. They had gone away, and had been away for some time when I was little. How was this...? I cannot think now. I did find them in the end, but that's a long—. No, you go on, please. Your brother.'

'I did not. Did I wish I had one? Cannot say I did. But it could have been a help; indeed it could. Another to play music with. Another to speak for me. Another at my arm. But no, let's have more from you.'

I cannot not remember. I know now that I have to face up to how things went and what I was. If I do not, I cannot go on. But will they?

'There's no more to say', I say. 'I had a brother. I would like to know something of yours.' I have turned here to the one on my left.

'Thank you. They are good men, noble and young. But I have not seen them in a long time. Let me think how this was... I had to

'You should not ask. This one here'll tell you that she left home to look for two men, and that she did find them in the end, if not some

restore them to father. They had had another father to see to them, but now was the time to have them home again. She'll tell you I had nothing to do with all this, but that's not so, not so at all.'

way before the end, for it goes on and on, the way this one'll tell it, and you'll be dead and in your grave before it all comes to an end. You'll find it all goes on and on to the end of time.'

'Thank you', I say to the one on my left. Then, so that she'll not be left out, I say 'thank you' to the one on my right. Before I may say more, they are at it again.

'Did you love your brother?'

'This is all such a bore....'

'Indeed I did', I say. 'Indeed I do, I should say, for he's still with us.'

I do not say this, but in a way he's not, not still with us. This is not the 'us' it was—if it's an 'us' at all. What I should say is: He's still with them. But do I think he is? Could I not hope he's left as well? Could he have come here by now, to find me?

But when, O, will you say what you have to say, which is how you have come here to find yourself, to find another you, which you hope these two could help you with?

They have stayed still as I went away with my thoughts, and now when I look at them again, it all goes as it did before.

'Tell us of this brother of yours; I would like to know more. Does he, tell me, have a lady love? Would he have left your father by now and be master in his own—?'

'I would give my soul to be away from here. If I could, I would go up and look for some things for this maid to wear, other than what she's come in.'

'Master!' I say. 'That was it! That was what I meant to ask you: What do you know of the Master? How could I find him?'

'There is no master here. There's no-one to tell us what to do. It's not like that. We rose up, you see. So we do not have a king here, not now. And nothing like a king. One day we did. But that's over.

'I'll help you all I may, but you'll have to do most of it yourself. Do you remember the thorny rose to the left of the path that took you on from the Well of the Sun? It's such a joy! Comes out when

There's been no king here for a long time.'

the snow's gone. It must be out by now.'

'Rose?' I say.

'Indeed. But that was all long before we had come to make a home here, so I should not say "we" but "they". They rose up, and out with the king it was. So there's no master now.'

'Indeed. Go to that rose again and say this: "Bare bier bore, Here to for, Tell me how to find, What I have in mind." Then think of what it is. This will make the rose speak.'

'Thank you', I say. 'This is good to know, and could well be a help. You never know.' I do not ask to go right away, as that could form some doubt in the mind of the one on the left. And still there's been almost nothing from them of what and where they have come from, the reason they left.

'Would you tell me,' I say, 'each of you, one at a time if you would, of your most sweet love, of the one you keep in your heart and will not let go, never mind what becomes of him? Would you do that for me?'

This should do it.

'If I have to.... A soldier. My love was a soldier. That means he had to be away from time to time. Did I tell you I was a king's daughter, so there was nothing they would not do for me, most of all when my soldier was away. Still, there was one there that did not wish me well at all. Not at all. I'll tell you the reason another time. But here's how it was. This one comes to me when I have gone to bed.—No, it's not what you think: there was nothing of that. He's come to take something of mine, which he'll take to the soldier and say he's had it from me and more. Do I have to go on

'With all that heart of mine I will! I will with joy! But how to say this? What will you make of my words when you have not seen him? Ask me and I will tell you! But what good is that? You would have to see him, to be with him, to have his breath on your face! He rose up to my window. At night. We had seen each other a little before. Before that, I did not know there could be such things—such a one as he! As I say, he rose up to my window. I see it now: we speak to one another of love; we say we will be wed in the morning. We have promised this and we are. There was never a

with this? He was honorable, my soldier. When two of you are like this, and you have longed for each other, it will have to come out as it should. That's how these things go. You know that as well as I do. So let's say that's all there was to it. My soldier's had to go away. He's made to doubt. He comes home again and, at last, there are things that will restore his mind. We may now be as one. All's well that'll end well.'

doubt in my mind but that he would prove true! He is there when I come, and we are wed. He is my true love; he is my lord, the one I will honour for all time, as he will me. He is my honey; he is my rose. You must keep that in your thoughts: my honey, my rose. And now I cannot remember what we did then. We are wed, and we have a night of love, and.... It was all good. I know that. But I cannot now remember.'

I think I know them. I know I know them now. The one took a long, long path that went here and there, all over. The other they would keep close—that was how it was then—and not let out of doors. The two of them come to the one end: dead with a dead youth by them—but this is not death for the one, and for the other it is.

But where does all this come from, that I did not know I had in my mind?

'Thank you, madam', I say. 'And thank *you*, madam. It was hard for you—for the two of you —to say all these things, to remember all these things, but you did, and I thank you. This meant more to me than I may say. But truly I should go now. Before it becomes night again—and you never know when night will come here, I find, never know how long it'll last. Indeed, it is night almost all the time. A brief day, and then night will come and would seem to last for months, so you would think.'

I look at them one last time, one and then the other. And they look at me, as if they could see in to my soul.

Have I seen you before?   Have I been you before?

My hand is at the door.

K

'Me the king!'

I have come out the door, and it's still night (if not night again), and here's another of them in my face, and he goes up and down, up and down, with his 'Me the king! Me the king!' And then I see over there another one that would seem to think he's sovereign, never mind that he lost his soul on the way.

'Please cast your eyes this way to see the true king. Thank you.'

And that's not all: now there are two more of them that call out from some way up the mountain:

'There's no more than one king here, and that's me!'

'Do not believe these heels! What they say is all false! If you wish to see the king, here he is! Me!'

And then there are still another two that call to me to look their way, and so I have turned to see them, and there they are, and they have something to say as well:

'Now let's have this right, shall we? We must call on Reason to help us here. Reason would have it that there cannot be more than one king at a time. That's how things are. There cannot be two. I believe we all know we are in the one state here, and one state will have to have one king, if it is to have a king at all, which some do not. One king, I say. Not two. And by no means more than two. There may be two in one day, if one king should have died that day, so that another will have to be king that day and go on from there. But still that's not two at one time, and there's no other way there may be two in one day. You could say to me—and some have—that you would like there to be two for a time, to see how that went, but I would have to tell you that this could never be, no how, no way. I hope you are with me. And I know you'll all wish to have your say on this one, but if I may keep on for a little more, this was all to prove that there never will be more than one king, never will be two, let us say, if these two have breath in them. Now, to be brief, how it is here goes thus: there's more than one of us that'll call out all the time that he's the king, which means not that there's more than one king but that there's more than one that *would be* king, if he had his way. Would you please keep this in mind? I hope you will.'

'Do we have to have all this? Look this way and you'll have to say: "He is by right the king!"'

And now that I have turned again, I see there's another I had not seen before.

'Please, please, all of you! You, over there, you call on "right", as you call it. But come on, right will tell you in no time at all that the king must be a soldier—'

'That's me, a soldier!'

'You think such a one as you becomes a soldier? No, I was the soldier of all of us here!'

'You never could see what I had in me! You never would believe in me! A soldier I turned out to be: a soldier king!'

'I was a holy king.'

'I thank God I was not there to see it!'

'I would pray night and morning.'

'God help us!'

'And *I* was a soldier!'

'You could never be a soldier!'

'You died young!'

'It's not so hard, you know, to make out here

which of us is king and which not. I have the majesty of a king, which means that I must be the king. That's all there is to it.'

At this I see that two more of them have come, out of nothing.

'Rose upon rose: it is time for the rose!'

Oh, the rose.... I remember. Thank you! I must find that rose.

'And heaven will tell you that the true lord here is—'

'Me! You cannot speak the words, o father mine. Your day is done. What you left I took up. Time will go on.'

The argument, as well, goes on, and I know I'll have to give it my all: 'YOUR MAJESTY!'

They all look my way.

But almost as they do so, they are blown away by other words that come to me, from one I know.

L

'O! O! Is this you?'

That call!

I cannot make out where it comes from, but the youth himself I know....

'My brother!' I call out to the night. 'Where are you? I cannot see you! Where are you? Where are you?'

'Here!' A hand is touching mine, and I take it with my other. There's almost no light, but his face is so close. No beard still. Never will have. May be he would if he stayed here, now he's come. But will he?

'Is this you?' I ask. '"You, you and no-one but you?"' That was something we would sing, at a time long gone. 'How did you find me?'

'I did, like, go all over. But then I think: Where

would she have left *from*? So I go up there, and I see with my little eye....'

'Oh, in the snow? There was still the snow? You could see my treads in the snow?'

'Right I could. So then it was, like, go! go! go! and let's see where that lady's gone to! There they all are—may be out there now, for all I know— one by one by one by one. It's like they ask me to go where you have gone. Like they say: Out of here, brother!'

'You know, I had no such wish at the time, but I see now—'

'"Oh, let me not show my hand!" Is that what it was? Come on, O, you are so out of it!'

'Like you, with your A–Men Two.'

'Do you *have* to remember that? My Sweet Lord!'

'And your Violets.'

'My youth, when I was—never mind. So that's what I do, like. And I made it here.'

'I did not think... Let's say I had no expectation you would do that. But now that you are here, my, it's good to see you!'

'And you!'

'Quoth!' I say.

'Quoth!' And now he's held up his hand for mine.

'But there's more to it than that', I say. 'What have you come *for*? Did *they* ask you?'

'There is, as you say, more to it than that.' And he's turned away from me to say this.

'Then what?'

There's more light, and I see him take a breath.

'Do I have to tell you, O? Come on, do I truly, like, have to tell you?'

Another breath.

'I know what you'll ask. That I should go and be with you all again, and it'll all be as it was? No. I cannot do that. And do you blame me?'

A little time goes by before he'll say: 'No'.

'Then that's all there is to say. You know what they are like. I have come away. And you may not know this, but so have you. How would it be if you stayed, if you stayed here with me?' (I do not at all know if I truly wish him to do this. There are things you have to do for yourself, and a brother could well be in the way.)

He's shaking his head. 'This is not my fairground. It's not where I have to be. And it's not where *you* have to be. You know that. We are made to be *there*, with them, in Denmark.'

'You made it out', I say. 'You have gone over the mountain. That's it. It's all over now, for you. Be here. Find yourself here!'

'No way!'

'Way!'

'O, there are things I have to do at home.'

'You still think of it as home?'

I look in to his eyes. What does he know? Does he still believe all this, that he's in Denmark there, with the King of Denmark, that he's a courtier?

'You have another reason to wish to be there', I say.

Will he show some honesty with me now?

We look at each other, and it's as if, with his eyes, he did say something of a love with such powers over him that he cannot speak. I see a tear.

Then it's over.

'The king—'

'Was he the one to ask you to come?'

'No! How could you think that? Let me tell you, O: I have come here of my own will! Out of love, love for you, you poor little gis! This is not, like, where you should be! Do you know where this is? From what I see, all they do here is remember and remember—all the time. There's a perfume of the dead and lost. But we are young, O! We are young! God, do you see what they call fashion here! This is not where you should be and, you know, still be you.'

'That's it!' I say. 'I have no wish to be me—me

as I was. I have to find another me. It's in here'—I lay my hand on my heart—'and it's up to me to find it. As of now I cannot tell what it is, this other me. It may be something I do not like. It may be something that it'll take me some time to see as right, to know to be right.'

'I love what you are, O.'

How could I doubt this?

'But do I now have to say to you:' he goes on, 'I love what O was?'

My sweet brother!

'I fear for you, O.' He's cast his eyes down and does not speak to me face to face. 'I fear you have, you know, lost your mind a little. Like, here you are: the O I think I know. But—Lord love us!—I do not know you, O. I do not know you at all. It may be I never have done.'

Lord love us. Something father would say. Hard to go on now. But I must.

'Which of us'—I look down—'could say what it is to know another—indeed, what it is to know one's own heart and mind?'

Then his eyes are on me again, and I have to look at him, and his face is harsh. 'I know what I must be. Do you?'

'There's no "must"', I say. 'We all may choose. You may choose.'

'Oh, you think so? How little you know!'

He's up as if to go, but then he's turned again to look at me. 'The king would like to see you again.'

'Him? He may have a reason.'

'And there's this. I wish I did not have to say this to you—'

'Father. Is he not well?'

'He is well; he is well.'

'Go on.'

'You remember how he comes to his death?'

'How could I not?'

'With him now it's like it's a true death, like he'll be dead and gone. Each time it's like that. Each time more so. He goes on with it—you know what he's like—but his heart's not in it now.'

I see in his eyes there's more he'd like to say. 'Go on,' I say, 'if you have more to tell me.'

'I know I should not say this, not to you, O, but it's, you know, like he's given up. Without you there. You should see him.'

'Do not ask that.'

'O, you should see him.'

'Please....'

'You should see him!'

'No.'

I meant to say 'I cannot' as well, but he's left me no time.

M

'My sweet one, o my sweet one!'

But did my brother go? Is he not still here, in this night that goes on as if it would never end?

And where are we now?

'Is that you, my brother?' I call out.

'It could be, could it not?'

But that's not him. And it's not like him to play with me this way.

'What are you? And what have you come for?'

'Ha!'

'Show me where you are!'

'Here. By you.'

'But you know I cannot see you at all.' I say.

'Then what if I do this?'

A rose light comes on, and we are in a bed chamber. A bed. Green bed clothes.

He's raised a hand and there's music:

The way I like it
Is the way it is
I have mine, (do it!),
He's had his...

It's all given me the horrors. To my mind—but what do I know?—it's like this is where a lady of the night would do what she had to do. I have to say I do not like being here at all. And I do not like the look of him.

'How did you do that?' I ask. 'You turned on the light. How the hell did you do that?'

'Ha! There's more I could do if you would let me, young madam.'

'Come close and you'll rue the day!'

'What would you do to me, then, young madam?'

'Do not call me that!'

'What?'

'Young madam.'

'If you say so. As you like—'

Before this goes on some more, I say: 'Look. There's a door over there.'

'Do you have to be like that?'

'Look: I have come here for a little help. Which I do not think I'll have from you.'

'You ask me to go?'

'I do.'

'Then I'll honour the lady and go.' Which he does.

I see the door close and then, in no time at all, there's a knocking at it.

'Let me come in! Please!'

'No.'

No more knocking.

I let some time go by, and then I go to the door. It's locked.

Now it's me knocking.

'Let me out! Let me out!'

'If you'll let me come in again.'

'No.'

'What if I do this?'

I look away from the door. The bed's gone. The green bed clothes have gone. It's all bare.

I cannot speak.

'Like it?'

I do not know what to say.

'If not, there's this one I could do.'

And in no time there's a scholar in here to give a lesson, and they all come in, and go on as if they cannot see me.

Then the scholar's turned to me. 'I like this one. Hope you do.'

It's him.

Whilst it would seem he goes on with his lesson, his words are all for me.

'Tell me: what did you come here for? Then we may go: you your way, me mine.'

With all that's gone on, I truly cannot think. My mind's not my own. Will he now help me? Not be as he was before? What's come over him? Was it something I did? And what did he ask? Oh, right. It'll take me some time to think which of many answers I should give. The things that have gone on here.... My brother. Before him these men that all think they should be king. Before them—Ha! It was one of the two ladies.

'A rose', I say. 'Could you tell me how to find the rose? There's a rose that will speak, so they say, and I have to find it for it to tell me the way I should go.'

'Where did you have that from?'

'Two ladies. They have a home with each other. They speak at the—'

'I know. Which of them?'

'I think it was the one on the right. But it may have been the one on the left. There's quite a difference.'

'There is. And you believe them? That is, you believe the one it was? You know, one of them cannot but speak true; not so the other.'

Mercy me, how should I know which was which?

Whilst my mind is up and down with all this, I say: 'I do not know, my lord, what I should believe'—but as I speak these words cold fear comes over me, and without a breath I say: 'I have nothing other to go on.'

'I like you, so I'll give you what help I may. All is not as it may seem. Keep your eye out. You have seen how you may be—'

'Deceived. I know.'

'Could be that's the reason you had to come here, to take a lesson—from this scholar, right? —in what is true and what's not.'

'How do I know what is true?'

'Look at it in the light. Look at it with your heart. Look at it with your mind. Look at it, if you may, with your soul. One of these will tell you.'

'Look, it's a little late in the day, but could I ask what to call you?'

'Rich. That's what they all call me here. Rich.'

'Well, thank you, Rich. I should be on my way. Could you let us out of here?'

As I speak it's all gone: the door, the table, all of it, and we are out on the grass, and the sun is up.

'Look out for yourself, O.'

He's held me by the wrist, then lets me go.

'You know me?'

'We all do by now.'

'How many more of you are there, Rich?'

'You'll find out. Not so many. Now, you look out for yourself.'

'"Yourself" you say. That's almost what I have come here to find. But it's hard. One day I think I may be on the up; then in the morning I'll be down again. Some of it's being here, where I never seem to know what to do, and where I cannot find my way, and you all—well, most of you—would like to help, but for some reason it's never turned out as it should, you know? Then again, it could be all me.'

'No, it's not you. It's how things are. We have all been there. But then you may choose—'

'Choose what?'

'Nothing. There are things I should not tell you, things you'll have to find out.'

I look at him, and he gives me a perusal that gives nothing away.

'Shall I see you again, Rich?'

And then I think better of it.

And know not to ask again.

Then he speaks: 'Tell me again: What did she say you had to find?'

'A rose.'

'Right. It may not be what you think. And that was not all. You would then know where to find....'

'The Master. It's him I have to see, but for some reason I have to go by way of this rose.'

'That again is how things are here.'

'Thank you, Rich. I know you know more than this but cannot tell me.'

'We are all on the look-out, O. That's what we are here for, all of us: to find what we most wish for. There's no one way. You'll have your way, which will not be my way—which means there's no more than a little help I could give you. Almost no help at all. But one day you'll be there. You may not find him at all. It may be that he'll find you.'

'Thank you for that, Rich', I say.

'But then what will you ask?'

'I'll ask.... I'll ask where and how I'll find another me. Not the me I have been. Another.'

'I see. I see it in your face, O. This is something you have to have.'

'It is.'

'That's how it is for all that come here. There's something we have to have, other than what we have had.'

'What's yours, Rich—if I may ask?'

'Never mind that. On with you.'

I have turned to go, but then I think of something I must ask.

'Rich, which was your play?'

By the time the words are out, there's nothing there.

N

That'll take it out of you, that will! Goodness, what a one he was!

I should tell you: she's gone for a little time. So you'll have to make do with me.

When it's all done, and he's gone, this...what did he call himself?...she comes over to me to say, right in my face: 'I have had it up to here!' As if I was the one to blame!

But I could see she was done in, so I say she should have a lay down, close these green eyes. I'll take over. She give me a look. It's all right, O, I say. (I call the lady 'O'. We all do.) I'll not tell one of my...you know.... No, it'll all be quite lady-like. Have no fear. So away she goes.

As she's not here, I could tell you what I make of all this.

But should I?

What the hell....

You see, it's all this 'other me' to-do. It's not for me, that. I have one me; what would I do with another? Could be they would speak, the one of them to the other. Could be they would not. May be one would have a go at the other. And where would I keep another me? And then there's this: What is a me? Do you see it? No. Will it speak? No! It's me that does that. That's to say, I think it is. Does it have a heart, a head, like I have? You tell me. Will it give you good counsel? Will it be there tomorrow? Will it go away, and you'll be left by yourself? God love us, this'll do my head in!

But here she comes, up from bed. Time for me to go.

○

I have come a long way, to where there's another mountain, and there's a light up there, so harsh I cannot look at it. I think it must be the light of the sun on a glass window, but I'll go up and see.

You may have to be patient here as I make my way up. Most of the time there's nothing to speak of. Oh, a robin over there. Would be good if it would sing. But no. Could be the cold.

There's no path, but if I keep on the stone I'll be all right. If you go on the turf, you find it comes away with your treads.

There's still the sun on that window, if that's what it is. It'll show me the way. Not so many come up here, so it would seem. If more did, they would, over time, make a path. Could well be no-one's been up here in months. Months and months. Does no-one look in on him, the one that's made his home up there?

I should have gone to look for that rose, but there's something that's made me come this way. Some draw. The sun on that glass window. The one that'll come to the door.

Do not know what I'll find. Could be a scholar, up here to take a close look at the sun. Better, he'll think, to do that on his own. Have all his time to himself. For the things he'll have to do. And there could be another scholar (you keep yourself to yourself), up here to look for flowers that have not been seen before.

If not a scholar at all, the one up here could be a watchman, to keep an eye out. There could be two of these observers. More. What do they have to look out for? Men from the Other Face.

I think some more, and in no time I have come all the way. Indeed this is a home, but I have to take a breath before knocking at the door. It would have been better to come up when the sun had gone down a little, but there we are. Here now.

From here I may see all the way over to that other mountain, which could be the one I had to come over from 'Denmark', if that's what we should call it—which I cannot see at all, as it's all the way down. I cannot see it, and it means nothing to me. That's where I was, and I did not know what it was. That's where my father still is, and no doubt by now my brother.

I have turned from it all. There's no window that the sun was on; this fair home, all the way up here, is all made of glass. No-one comes here, so he must not mind if he's seen.

Oh, but the one in there is a young lady, on a bed, but she's up and quite composed. I seem to think I know this young lady from before.... But where? Could she have been the one with the flowers? The one that stayed up over my head as I went? The one in white? It's hard, in my memory, to tell one from another.

So it's not a he up here. How one still falls in to this! But she could still be a scholar. She could still be a soldier. And I may find out before long.

There's the door. Over I go.

At my knocking the young lady rises. She comes to the door. We look at one another, face to face.

What is this? Fear? Ecstasy? Are we head over heels in love with one another in no time at all? Is she blown away like me? I think she is.

I should say right away that there's nothing of dalliance in this. She's no libertine and never will be. I see that.

She's held out a hand to me, but then she took

it away again, as if touching would be more than she could do with.

Which of us will speak? She does.

'Oh my God! You look like me!'

'No', I say, 'you look like me!'

'You could change clothes with me—', at which I take over, '—and no-one would see the difference!'

'You know what I'll say!'

'Most of it!' I say.

'The two of us wear green and white!'

'All the time, me!' I say.

'Me too. But come in! Come in! This is all too... I do not know what! Look: let me hold the door for you!'

And so I go in.

Now that I have done so, it's as if this is *my* home as well, the home I now remember, but did not before—as if the memory, long lost, comes to me again.

Think of it. I cannot tell you what it's like; you have to think of it, think of how it would be if you could see yourself in another's face, if you could look at another hand and think it was yours—if you could look at another hand and *know* it was yours. If two could be one, and never more than one.

We go, hand in hand, to that bed I had seen. 'Lay yourself down, and I will too.' The words seem to come to me from over that other mountain, but she is right here by me.

We are in that state of grace that I wish I could speak of, but I know no words that would do it.

I have no wish to do other than she'll ask. We look at each other.

'What are you? Where have you come from?'

I do not know which of us these words come from.

'Give me your hand again.' 'Take my hands in yours.' 'Do you mind if I lay my hand on your face like this?' 'No, I do not mind at all.' 'May I do that again?' 'You do not have to ask.'

More words, that no-one may say they own.

'What may I call you?' Now I know this is she.

'O', I say. No more than that.

'O! O! O! Is it a sigh? Is it the night-time call of an owl? O! O! O!'

'And you', I say. 'What should I call you?'

'There's never anybody here to call me anything.'

'Then what do you call yourself?' I ask.

'O-fie.'

I cannot quite say it the way she does, with a long 'O' and a long 'I' that goes on and on, but I give it a go: 'O-fie.'

'O-fie and O', I say. 'O and O-fie. Which is it? Let's have no argument!'

'No, no, as you say! Anything but that!'

'Well, then', I say, 'I'll be two if you'll be one.'

'And I'll be one if you'll be two.'

'Then that's done with', I say. 'Tell me all you may of yourself.'

'You'll know it already.'

'All what?'

'Already. Like: by now, from before. Already.'

'I'll remember', I say. 'There are words of yours I do not know.'

'We have been away from each other a long time.'

'Indeed we have. But now we are with one another—'

'—and we'll go on that way for good and all!'

'O-fie!' I say. 'Sweet O-fie!'

'My O! My dear heart!'

It goes on like this for day upon day. Each morning I think: I should have left by now. Each night I find I have not.

And it's hard to tell how long I have been here. A day is like another day. A night is like another night.

'All is still', I say to O-fie. 'There's no "is" and "was" and "will be".'

'It's Mountain Time, O.'

I wish I could go on like this. I know I cannot.

Tell yourself, O! What have you come here for? It was to find another you: remember? O-fie is not that other you. You did say that. You did say so yourself. She's a joy, but this path the two of you are on—the one of you, you could say—is not the right way, not for you. Before long you'll have lost the will to go. She'll see this as well, and she'll think she's to blame. Should she make you go? Should she close the door and keep it locked?

'O-fie, do you think we could have some music?' I ask. 'This morning's one when, if you are like me—and I know you are—, you deject yourself, never mind what you do.'

'Oh, my O! But what did you ask for?'

'Some music.'

'Do I know what that is?'

All right. This is one of the words I know and she does not. There are some where it's the other way.

'Music, O-fie', I say. 'La-la-la, la-la-la. I would like you to sing to me. Will you?'

'The ear's appetite!' And now it's me that's lost.

But sing she does.

It's a green day when I see you,
A white when you are away,
The small light at the window,
The cold of come-what-may.

We stood upon the mountain,
You leave to go on down.
All I have now's remembrance,
And you, you are on your own.

'Is that how it'll be, do you think?'

That could have been O-fie, could have been me. Other things:

'Are you more yourself now, with me by you?' Again, I cannot tell you which of us this would have been.

'I love you in that green shirt. It's so you.' This was me. That I know.

'You took the very stoniest path up here, you know. You found the way, but here's another I'll show you.' O-fie. Had to be.

'Will you unclasp your hands, my dear? You are secure here. You know that.' O-fie again.

'While I was all alone here, did you *know* that I was?'

'No. Never.'

'If you had, would you have sought me out?'

'How could you ask that!'

'Tell me something. Make it up if you like. It does not have to be true.'

'When I speak, you think this is yourself.'

'That could be true.'

And then there are things we play, like:

'How many words can you make with these letters?'

'What letters?

'These letters.'

'A, B, I, O, S, T.'

'And N, and W, and Y.'

'Saint.'

'Away.'

'Nony.'

'What's that?'

'Look it up.'

'I will.' Then: 'It's one of your words, not mine! I object! Sophister!'

'Shall we take a poll?'

'A poll of two?'

'That do not wish for more', she said.

I cannot tell you the effect of these last words on my soul.

And she'll make up things the way I do:

'Time out of mind, there was a prince. I do not know what he was a prince *of*, but never mind that. There's no reason for us to know. It may be better not to.

'Now, most of the time, in something like this, if there's a prince he'll be noble and fair and earnest and steadfast and attentive to the ladies and do good things. This prince was not like that. He had a beard and was careless....'

Now and then I was not up for it. I had to go. But I had no wish to go. I stayed:

'There was a worthy man of wit and wealth withal, and thence—'

'Another time, O-fie. What it is to be down like this....'

And there are so many other things I remember from how she would say them:

'It is a privilege I have received.'

'Lovers' tokens are not to be lent only but given.'

'Your shoes!' (I call them 'shoon'.)

'What do you mean when you say you are a maiden fearful and pitiful? Are you not ready?'

'We have vowed that if one of us dies the other will not be lagging.'

'Christen me again then!'

'Till mid-morning. At the latest.'
'My flower.'
'I would be bereft.'

'Tell me another one, O-fie.'
'Tell me one of yours.'
'I will do.'
'Promised?
'Promised.'
'Would you take vows on it?'
'I would.'
'Well, then:

'Out there in a time without time, the Green Lady is still alive. At night she will look for an opportunity, and in the morning it could be that your heart will have been stolen. Cold, dead cold you will be, but walking, you could still be walking. You still have a pulse. You are not laid out, and your dear love grieves over you. There will be no alteration in you to show that the Green Lady would have been in bed with you all night and stolen your heart.

'No-one—*no-one* parts with their heart with a good grace. It will have to have been filched from you. You will have to have been distracted by what she did to you. She grips you. Silent, she will have moved in to your bed, and she grips you, and right then she will have stolen your heart, and little by little you will be forgetting it all, for that, too, she will have charge of: your mind, and what it will remember.

'In the morning they may say to you: What is the reason your window is all splintered? Did anybody cast a stone at your window and dashed away? Did *you* do this? And you will not remember anything: not these green hands on you, not how you grow there, not how she stood as she untied these green garters, not how she jests with you before, not how she could teach you there is more to your nature than you could believe, not the cunning in these green eyes, not the quick green showers that would come over you, short but so pleasant, not the gallery in full green light in which you seemed to be fixed firm as she did what she did, not the great green jewel that adorned that green breast, not how she holds you, not how she's touching you as she's gathering your heart from within you to leave you cold and with no remembrance.'

Ungartered she was.

There are some things I do not speak of to O-fie. Most of all, how we all here may have come from some play or other. I still cannot quite believe this, but that's not the reason. I have not raised it as I have no wish for us to speak—to think—of things that have nothing to do with how we are right now.

For me, to be up here is to be away from all my doubt and fear down there on the ground. Here I may love O-fie without shame. And it's so for O-fie as well, I know. We are so close.

But I have stayed here a long time—over-long. This was not what I have come here to do—to find. I have to go.

I do not think it out. I may have left some of my things. But here I go, down the mountain. I have not turned to see if she is there to look out from that glass home. I have not turned, and I will not do so.

P

I have not come all the way down what I will now think of as O-fie's Mountain when it's as if all the bells of hell call out. There, a long way out, the 'Lady Grace' is being blown this way and that, tumbled up and down. Men draw on something I cannot quite see, and as they do so they sing:

> *Be———lay, there! Be———lay!*
> *Ay, ay, be———lay, oh! Be———lay!*
> *Keep us from recks!*
> *Reckless we'll be!*
> *Ay, ay be———lay, oh! Be———lay!*

They sing it twice, thrice, more, whilst there's one at the wheel, each arm bended to it by the bulk of his shoulders. Now and then he'll call to the men, but it's hard to make out all his words as the other men sing on.

'Let go down there! Give them more play! For the love of God, give them more play!'

Mercy me, what a night!—for now it is night. But there's a harsh light on the 'Lady Grace', so that I see all there is to see out there.

I call as well, to the one at the wheel.

'Hey there! Is there something I could do to help?'

I see him take his eyes away from the wheel and look my way.

'No, madam, thank you. Not from where you are! We'll come out of this! You'll see! All we must do is be patient!'

Patient! When you are in a state like this!

Then I think: Could this be the Master? To have such powers of command! The 'Lady Grace' would have to have a master, but could this be *the* Master, the one I have to find?

I have raised my head to call out again with all the powers I have: 'Are you the Master?'

'I have to be right now!' Again he's turned to me. 'No, we lost him before sun up, when we come in to all this. Shame. It would make you weep, if you had time for a tear. He was one you could look up to. But he went over, poor soul.

O'erthrown he was. No-one was there to see him go. We turned, but we could not see him. He must have gone down right away. I was the Two on this show, so it was up to me. But let me see to this!'

He turned the wheel to the right, and then he could speak again.

'We should have come in where you are'—and where's that? I think—'but in all this we cannot. We'll have to keep out here and see if it goes down a little.'

'I wish you well!' I call to him as I go on down again. 'I know you'll make it!'

'Thank you, lady! Could I ask you something?'

'Please do!'

'If you see my daughter, would you say you have seen me? You could say: He will not let you down. Not like last time. He'll be there. Would you do that for me?'

'How will I know your daughter? What does she look like? What do you call this daughter of yours?'

But I cannot see the 'Lady Grace' now, and no answers come.

Q

I have come all the way down, and here's a door, with the words 'The King's Head' over it, and I go in to find young men (as most of them are) in there to make merry.

Show me the way to go home,
It's late and I have to go to bed,
I had a little glass, you know, it may be two,
And it's gone right to my head!

There's a lady with a key in one hand; she would seem to be the head of this commerce. I go over to this lady and say 'Good morning!'

'Here's a good one! She comes in, and what does she say? "Good morning!"

'Ha, ha, ha!' from most of them there.

She's turned to look at me again.

'Nay, love, it's tomorrow night!'

More 'ha, ha, ha!' from the young men.

I think I should go before this becomes worse, but she's at my arm now.

'It's all right, love. Let's find you a table. Come with me.' She took my hand, and we go over to a table with no-one at it.

By now the young men have gone on to other things.

> *On now, Christian soldier:*
> *Down their stockings falls!*
> *Take two, have another,*
> *Fair-faced ladies all!*

'This do you?'

'If I'll not be in the way of this lady here...'

'Oh, give no mind to that one. She's well out of it by this time of night. And you know what they say: She's no better than she should be. Now, what would you like?'

'How does he do Cockle-in-Violets?' I ask. 'Dupped, gyved, larded, unbraced...? I could go for something like that!'

'We are right out of it, my love. We'll have more in in the morning, but that's no good, is it? So what would you say to some Long End Fair.'

Long End Fair? What could she have meant?

'Long End Fair: 'are. See? It's the way we speak down here. I could say: I like the look of your hope and grace. Hope and grace: face. You'll see it in no time. If not, I'll coach you.'

'Thank you', I say. But is this where I should be? I do have to have something; that's true. I have had nothing all the time I have been here. But 'Long End Fair'? May be not. Still, should I say no?

'Thank you', I say. 'Indeed, could I please have some of that "Long End Fair", if there's some left?'

'There is. Good, good. Would not have done for me to tell you of it if there had *not* been, would it? And with that?'

'A glass of.... What do you have?'

'We have Cold Countenance; we have White Honey (that's a Flowers); we have Closet Door. That's not all, but the ladies seem to like these.'

'Not imports, are they?'

'No, my love! Naught but good home things here!'

'Then I'll take a glass of White Honey, please.' And I think to ask: 'Will that go well with the Long End Fair, would you say?'

'With the what? La! You had me there! I'll have to keep my eye on this one!'

With that, she left.

> *The maid went over the mountain,*
> *The maid went over the mountain,*
> *The maid went over the mountain,*
> *To see what she could see...*

I had some time, then, to look at where I was. I doubt these young men will know the Master, but may be one of them'll know something—like if it's true you could find a rose that would speak, up by the Well of the Sun. Such a long time's gone by.... How long have I been with O-fie?—when I should have been down here, to do what I have come to do.

Now here she comes again, with the Long End Fair and the White Honey.

'Thank you!' I say. 'That does look good!'

'Given you a little end of good-god as well.'

I look down at what's now on the table.

'Oh! That one's not so hard. Good-god! I love good-god! Thank you!'

'It's been out all day, but I think it'll be all right.'

'Would now be a good time to ask you some things?' I ask.

'Not now, love. And you should give your mind to that, I should think. Not let it go cold. I'll be here again.'

'Oh, before you go, what should I call you?'

'You could call me "Heaven and Hell". See?'

'I *do* see, Heaven and Hell!'

She goes away again, and I have turned to what's before me.

Does not take me long before it's all gone.

Then one of the young men comes over, and he's down on his knees at my table. I truly do not like this. O God, I see he'll sing.

I see the light on the night that I go by
that window,

'Look at you!' Heaven and Hell is here again. 'Now, my love, what was it you had on your mind?'

I see the long-lost remembrance of love
on that door,

'Well, thank you,' I say, 'but what are we to do with, you know, him here?'

She was my lady,

'Let him be; he's like this all the time. But ask away, my love. What's on your mind? I see there's something.'

As she deceived me, I see it, went out of
my mind.

She's bended down so that we may speak.

My, my, my, Rosemary!

'Two things. I have not been here long, so this is still find-your-way time for me.'

By, by, by, Rose—

But he cannot make it to the end before he falls over. One arm's up ... and down again. Then there's no more from him.

'Should we help him up, give him a hand?'

'Better not, love. You never know what they'll do in this state. But what did you say?'

'How I have not been here long. Still have to find my way.'

'Like that for all of us when we come here.'

I let a little time go by, so that she could say more if she would. Then I go on.

'Well, there was a lady—two ladies, I should say, but one of them was the one to tell me—and I remember it well—I should look for a rose that could speak.'

'Where? Did she say?'

'This was when I had been to the Well of the Sun. So it would have to have been close by there, I should think.

'That's some way from here. Not my day-to-day ground at all. Cannot help you there, my love. But *two* things, you did say.'

'I did. You see, I have come here to find another me.'

'Another you! I quite like the one you have!'

'Well, thank you, but the one I have is not right for here. No, that's not it. It's not right for *me*. It was *given* me, in another.... This is all so hard to say. But what I would like to ask you is if you know of the Master—if you know the Master himself.'

'Know what, my love? You think more than's good for you. Now, I should go and call time. But come again another night. We'll have Cold Play here. You know how they'll *never* play now, not in a little how's-your-father like this. But I know how to make men do what I like—what they like, as well. All the way, if you are with me.'

Of that I have no doubt.

> *He'll be knocking up that madam when*
> *he comes,*
> *He'll be knocking up that madam*
> *when he—*

'No more of that, if you please! Time! Time! Out the door, all of you! Take your things and be gone! Time! Time! See you again! Time! Time! Time!'

R

On my way out, when I have almost tumbled on something, my arm's held by one of the young men, and I look at him.

'Thank you!' I say.

'Would you like me to see you home?'

He's a sweet face, and I wish I could take him up on it, but you never know what you'll let yourself in for.

'No thank you', I say. 'Truly.'

There's this as well: I have no home.

But I should say something more, not to let him down more than I have to, so I say: 'And it's still light.'

'When it's not, then.'

Is this a come-on?

'Right. Some other time', I say.

'You let me know. You'll find me in here, like as not.'

And he's gone.

'Oh, you think so?'

'What?' I look up and down. 'Where are you?'

'Up here, in your head. I did say I would come with you.'

'And I did say "no".'

'I never take "no" for answers—not from ladies. And you should think. Down here by yourself? That will not do, lady, that will not do. You'll have to have me with you. So here I'll be.'

'And you made your ungracious way in to my head how?'

'Think I'll let on?'

'I should not ask?'

'And I'll not tell.'

'May be it will be a help to have you with me.'

'Believe me, it will. You'll see. A help in many a way. Like, would you be up for a go right now?'

'No, I would not!'

'As you like.

'The lady when the light went on
'Had one hand on his—'

'Will you please not sing!' I say. 'It's more than I should have to take. You make your way in there —I cannot tell how—and what do you do? What all men do when they take their showers!'

'What's that then?'

'If you cannot keep a better tongue in your head—'

'*Your* head, lady. And what would you like me to do with that tongue, whilst here?'

'Keep it still!'

And he does. My expectation went all the other way. And I say nothing, as I take the path away from the 'King's Head'. It's a fair night. I could almost sing, but—could he tell what I think?— he's the one that does, and not as he did before.

> *Here comes the sun, do–do–do–do,*
> *Here comes the sun, and I say:*

'Over to you!'
So I take it up.

> *It's all right.*
> *Little doublet, it's been a long, cold, wretched*
>   *snow time,*
> *Little doublet, in many months it's not*
>   *been here.*

'You again!'

Here comes the sun, do–be–do–be,
Here comes the sun...

'I could go on like this a good long time', I say.
'So could I.'
And we sing as we go.
'By the way,' I say, 'what should I call you?'
'Robin. That's what they all call me here. Robin.'
'Then I'll call you Robin as well.'.
'And you?'
'O'.
'Good to know you, O!'
'How long have you been here, Robin?'
'Long! I could tell you had things on your mind!'
I'll have to be patient.
'No, but when did you find your way here?' I ask him.
'It's been some time, but not so as to have lost me my youth. That's all I know. And you?'
'Could be it's not been more than a day. May be two. Hard to tell, when the sun would not seem to keep time at all, but rises and goes down as it will.
'I had to come here', I go on. 'I did not know what it would be like.'

'It is what it is.'

'Do you remember not being here?' I ask.

'Remember? Do I know what it is to remember? Do I *remember* what it is to remember?'

'You are all in the now, Robin.'

'I believe so.'

'Wish I could be like that.'

'I like you as you are, O. Let me say this: I love you as you are.'

'I think I could see the Master, when I was up the mountain.'

'You cannot see the Master, O. Did you not know that?'

'How's that? Is he made of glass?' Keep it light.

'No! It's that he's not here.'

'He's not here, but there *is* a Master?'

'There *is* a Master. The one Master. How could there not be a Master, *the* Master?'

'But he's in some other....?'

'That's all I know. He's not here.'

'But I have to find him!' I say.

'O, I have nothing to say. There's no help I have to give you on that one.'

'What do you know of the rose?'

'What?'

'The rose that will speak if you ask it.'

'And if you do not?'

'I have to find that rose', I say.

'There's no more I know.'

'Then I'll be on my way. Thank you for all that you have done for me. So long.'

'But you have to take me with you, O! You'll have to have your Robin!'

S

'Do you know him, O? See him before?'

'Are you still here?'

'Where would you like me to be, O?'

'Up there will do for now, Robin. But him: no, I have not seen him before.'

We have come on some way when these words from Robin make me look to the right to see a steward, as he could be, of some stature. There's something in his right hand, and he'll look down, remember the words, and then look up again, to speak them—to himself as it would seem. But of all this I cannot make out more than a little, here and there.

'...o when will you come to me?...' Nothing before this.

'No, Robin, I have not seen him before. You?"

'...before me, and the shame of my...'

'Does *not* look like one you would find in the King's Head.

'...the memory of them from the...'

'I would not think so, Robin, no. But I'll speak to him.'

'...in thee: let me not be...'

As we come close and see his face, Robin becomes a little jangled:

'Know what, O? I think we should keep away. Let's not be....'

'...all the night make I my...'

'He's all in a night of his own, O!'

'...o Thou, my God...'

'We should not have come over!'

'...For their heart was not right with him...'

'It's all right, Robin. Truly. He's one of these men of God.'

'You think so?'

'...So they shall make their own tongue to...'

'I know so.'

'...I may tell all my...'

'What'll he tell us, O?'

'...And my tongue shall speak of thy...'

'He does not speak to us...'

'...God: God is not in all his thoughts...'

'...but to God.'

'...Many there be which say of my soul, There is

no help for him in God....'

'Would you see if he'll help, O?'

'...help us, o God of...'

'I could ask.'

'...Ask of me, and I shall give...'

'Grave father,' I say to him. 'May I ask you something?'

'...you more and more, you and your...'

'It's this. I have come here in the hope—in the expectation, I would say, I would find another me."

'...another god...'

'I have gone here and there, and have come to believe I would receive help from the Master.'

'...for he shall receive me...'

'But no-one, so it would seem, will tell me where this Master is.'

'...so would we have it: let them not say, We have...'

'If indeed he is here at all.'

'...Indeed speak...

'...in thy light shall we see light...

'...the night shall be light...'

'Oh, Robin! I'll not find this out from *him*!'

'...shall find out all...'

'He'll give no mind to me!'

'...out of mind I...'

'Go on, O! Do not give up now!'
'...up to the heaven, they go down again to the...'
'Do you have the powers to help me here?'
'...him for the help of his...'
'Do you know the Master yourself?'
'...make me to know mine end, and the...'
'If so, what could you tell me?'
'...I would not tell...'
'I have to give up, Robin.'
'...One...With Light...'
'...Over...Will Look...'
'No, O! This is to tell us!'
'...Over With...Love...'
'Tell us what?'
'...Over...Will Love...'
'It's like the green light to go, O! Do you see?'
'...Out...With Light...'
'...One...Will Look...'

T

If I could have locked his hand in mine I would have done, as we come away and say, the two of us as one: 'Owl!'

'But where to find him?' Thus Robin. 'That mark did not tell us. Down there to the left, do you think?'

'We'll give it a go.'

Away we go, and when that path gives out, we find another.

'You think we should call out "Owl!" as we go?'

'What good would that do? And could you call out from in there? Think.'

'Have you been out to find an owl in the night-time? No? Then please keep the lesson for when you have.'

It's good now to have Robin with me. If we could keep it that way to the time we find the

Master, that'll do for me.

'What was that?'

'Did you see something, Robin?'

'No, but it was like there are eyes on me. Then gone. Then more eyes that look at me.'

'It's nothing', I say. 'It's being out here in the night, when we do not know where we are, where we should go.'

'I know.'

'There, Robin!'

'What?'

'Did you not see him?'

'No.'

And now, as if he answers Robin, comes the call of an owl: 'To-what to-we!'

I look up.

'Do you see him, O?'

'No. There's no light!'

'But he must be up there.'

And the call comes again.

'O owl!' I say. 'Will you tell me where to find the Master, the one I *have* to see, the one I have come here for?'

No call. Nothing.

'It's no good, O.'

'May be not, Robin. Could be this is not the right owl. There must be more than one.'

'Must be.'

'And do we know he meant to say "owl"?'

'You tell me.'

What? This would have made us look at one another—if we could.

'Was that you, Robin?' I ask.

'Not me, no.'

'Then it must have been the owl! He *does* speak!'

'*She* does. Rose the owl here. And what, pray, are you?'

'O', I say. 'You may call me "O", if you would, madam.'

'And me: Robin.'

'Where are *you?*'

Well, this is a hard one to believe, I know, but there's a youth in my head, and now an owl that will speak.

Robin answers: 'In here', but Rose cannot see what he means.

'I do not have to know', Rose goes on. 'I'll say what I have to say to this young lady down there. Now, as you are here, would you like me to sing to you?'

How could I say no?

Rose is quite still. She lets out a little *'do–me— see–me–do.'* Then it's time to sing:

Fair youth, o fair youth,
With flowers on your bed,
But one you have not:
A rose that is sweet.

My love I have lost,
The fair youth did say,
She's gone and away:
Pale owl of the night.

We are being musicked by an owl.

'Thank you!' I say. 'It's not at all what you think it'll be.'

'It's not?'

'I meant, I had not had an owl sing to me before, so I had nothing to go on.'

'I see. It's all in the tongue, you see. But it would take me all night to tell you all the things you would have to remember if you would like to sing as an owl does.'

'I have no doubt.'

'But what have you come here for? Tell me that. Now that you have let me sing to you, you may ask me all you like.'

'Thank you. It's this: I have come here to find another me—'

'Come from when? Come from what?'

What should I say? 'Denmark, then. But I doubt you'll know where Denmark is.'

'Lord, that's rich! You do not know what I know!'

'That's true. Shame on me!'

'Oh, let it go, let it go! Come on, young lady, where do you hope to find this other me, as you call it."

'I believe the Master will give it me; if not, that he'll show me where to find it. And I believe you have access to the Master. Will you please tell me which way to go?'

'You do not go to the Master. He will come to you.'

U

It's hard to tell quite where you are. You may come upon something you think you have seen before, but there'll be a difference. Flowers up in no time; the path falls where before it rose. It's hard, as well—still more so—to tell where you should go.

The Master will come to you, they tell you. Right. How will he find you? Where should you be to make yourself seen? On the grass and not in doors, you would think. But should you go up O-fie's Mountain again?

'What do we do now, O?'

'I do not know, Robin, I do not know.'

'It's time I was home.'

What time would that be, then? What is time here? But it's true that I never did ask him, not from when he dove in to my head the way he did, how long before he would have to go, what he would have to go and do, where his home was, was he on his own. It's been all me, me, me.

All this with the 'rose', the Master.... It's had me on the go all the time. When I was at O-fie's, that was the last time I had a night in bed. You keep on; you never seem to wear yourself out. But we cannot go on like this. Poor Robin!

'Robin, you truly do have the right to go now. It's me to blame, to have had you out so late and so long. It's been good to have you with me, but all good things must come to an end.'

'But look, O, down on the ground there!'

I do look, and see what Robin's seen: a form with words on it.

'Take it up, O, take it up! It may tell you what you have to do so that you'll see the Master!'

I do as he says.

'What is it, O, what is it? Tell me, tell me!'

'Will you please be patient, Robin? I'll tell you, but I have to give it some perusal. Right. This is how it goes:

'"By command of him that could command,

'"Know that we come to you with good will,

'"Know that we see all that you do here, all that you say, all that you speak to, all that you say to them and all that they say to you; all this we know,

'"Know that we know where you go here, up and down, in and out,

'"Know that we see your brother when he comes here,

'"Know that we know of that wretched other brother you have with you right now,"'

'That's me, O. Would have to be me.'

'"Know that we, as well, are with you night and day,

'"Know that we have your good at heart,

'"Know that we see what you do here as noble,

'"Know that we think it would be right to show you mercy,

'"Know that we, like you, do not think that there should be more than one king—in the one state, that is,

'"Know that where you are now—where we are—is a state that is not a state,"'

'Will it go on for long like this, O?'

'Not so long, Robin.'

'Good.'

'Be still now, there's a good Robin.'

'"Know that we do not come to you with sword in hand and do not have to see you on your knees before us,

'"Know that, should you think to do so, we will not let you wed whiles you are here."'

'Will I not have your hand, then, O? Will you not let me make you the Lady Robin?'

'Give over!

'"Know that we love you, as we love no other,

'"This is all we have to say to you,

'"This is all we will say to you,

'"Up to when another day shall come."

'That's the end', I say, 'That's it.'

'So it did not tell you it's from the Master?'

'No, it did not. But *look*: it must be.'

'I would think so. I would take an oath on it.'

'See this here: "By command of him that could command."'

'Must be the Master, then, O.'

'But come to think, there's one way to take that "could", and then there's another way. Could be it means "with the powers to". But could be it means: "had the powers at one time but does not now". Do you see, Robin?'

'Think so.'

'If it's that—"had the powers at one time"—then this would be from the one that *was* the Master and not from the one that *is*, now. And so we would have to look for another Master.'

'*You* would, O. I have to go.'

'I know, Robin. You have been such a help.

What could I give you? What could I say more than "thank you"?'

'That'll do. It was up withered it was. I'll tell them all I had a long, long time in a maid—and then she was not a maid at all.'

'Remember me, Robin.'

'I'll remember you, O. I'll remember you. Out the door and—here I be.'

And there he is.

'Robin—'

'Now you see me—'

And now I do not.

V

And here, in no time at all, is another youth, so that, as I think my hand's touching Robin's, I find it's touching this other one's.

'Thank you for that', comes from him. 'A sweet breath of affection, when I have been here so little time.'

'It was not meant for you', I say.

'But I was the one to take it.'

'What have you come for?'

'What do you think? You turned me on.'

I give nothing away.

'Think that was it?' he goes on. 'Could be.'

Again I say nothing.

'But let's say it was to see you, to be with you. Us two. They all tell me of your beauty, your grace. Such things you have to see for yourself, close up.'

'Now you have seen me. Please go', I say.

'Is that how you think you should speak to me? You do not know what I could be.'

'I do not mind what you are. I know you cannot be the Master.'

'Ha, ha, ha! No, this is not the Master you see here before you. But what if the Master should ask some other to come and see you before he does?—to come and ask you this and that?'

I say nothing.

'What if I should say this to you?' he goes on. '"'Tis in my memory locked."'

At this I find my mind is jangled, worse than in quite some time.

'What are you?' I say.

'No, my sweet. Your words now should be: "And you yourself shall keep the key of it."'

'What are you?' I ask again.

'Come on, you know you have been observed. You have it in your hand, what we left for you, to tell you how things are.'

'I tear it up. Now', I say, and I do so.

'And what do you think that's done for you?'

'I do not know you', I say. 'I have never seen you before.'

'That is true. Here is one not of your cast.'

'Cast?'

'You know what that means. You have not lost all your memory.'

'I ask one more time: What are you?'

'You could call me your Valentine. How would that be?'

'I'll call you Valentine', I say. 'The "my", I think, may be left out. But this still does not tell me what you are, where you have come from, and what made you think you could hope for something from me.'

'Well, my little O, as you call yourself now, it may be that this will help you: "I do not know, my lord, what I should think." Remember that? If not, let me go on: "No, my good lord, but as you did command I did receive his letters."'

'It's not "receive"', I say.

'No? What is it then?'

'"Repel"! "Repel"! As you repel me!"

'There! You see! You *do* remember! "He hath, my lord, of..." But me oh my, I cannot think—'

'Go to hell', I say.

'Now, now, it would be better if we stayed of one mind as we do what we must, would it not? You know how this'll have to go. And it does not have to take such a long time as all that.'

'What does not?' I ask.

'For me to take you with me to where you

should be. You know where that is. Indeed, there's nothing I may say that you do not know before I say it—well before I say it. To give you another take: "My honoured lord, I know right well you did." How does it go then? Remember? "And with them words of so sweet breath..."'

'"...composed..." No! No! No!' I give him one on his wretched face, but he goes on:

'"...As made the things more rich." We may come to an end for now, if you would like. If not, we may go on some more. But it could well be we will not have to. It's all up to you.'

'Do you come from the Master?' I ask.

'That's for me to know and you to find out.'

'I left all that', I say. 'The words you would wish me to remember, the daughter that had to obey, the young soul locked in to something over which she had no command, the love—the love!—that no-one would receive from me: I left all that. I went out in the snow.'

'We *did* see you.'

'I went out in the snow, and I had to choose. It was hard. I will not tell *you* how hard it was. But I went on, and that is how I have come here, away from all that. I had to find—well, I will not go in to that, not if you know it all before I speak'

'It was to look for "another you". I know. We all

know. You did not keep this to yourself, did you? And what did you think this "other you", this "other me", would be like? Tell me! Please! It may be I could help.'

'Go away', I say again.

'That, I fear, I cannot do. Not without you. You would have to come with me.'

'Where?'

'You know where. "Indeed, my lord, you made me believe so."'

'No more!' I say.

'They are all there still. They cannot go on without you. Think how this must be for them: the king and his madam—all right, they may not have been so honorable in what they did to you —*to* you and *with* you—but what of the young lord—you know he had his eye on you—'

I *will* not remember. I *will* not be made to remember by him.

'Will you please take yourself away?' I say.

'—and what of your brother? We could see how it all went when he was here. Touching. How do you think he will have turned out now, when you had him go away?—had him go away without your help and your love?—not to speak of your poor father. Did you never think you should take him with you? You could *do* that if you would give yourself another time there. "Oh, woe is me, to have seen what I have seen, see what I see."'

I say nothing. I look at him. I keep my eyes on him.

'All right', he goes on. 'Then there's this—I think you'll know where it comes from: "They say a made a good end." Remember? But is it not: "They say *he* made a good end"? Which would you, to give you one of your own words, choose?'

'Not such a difference', I say.

'No, but it is one. You see: you are not one by yourself, my sweet O. There are two of you. May be many more.'

'So are we all. I is a chorus.'

'You think? I have come to restore you to yourself.'

At this there is a shaking, and all falls, is tumbled, blasted, and as if from the ground there comes this long, long sigh: 'Go!'

I cannot see Valentine. He's been blown away.

Words come to me that I do not wish for, but that seem right: 'Gramercy. God b' wi' ye.'

W

Indeed, there's no-one to be seen now, but the words go on that come from down there.

'I had to do that. I hope you are not affrighted.'

'No, not at all. God, how he importuned me! I should thank you. That was all more than I could do with.'

I look down at the grass as I speak, for this—this what?—this profound being cannot be seen.

'That's all right, then. I did think you could take it.'

'It would take more than that to have me in a state by now', I say, and then: 'Could I ask: Are you the Master?'

'Some say so. Not me. I do not.'

'From what I have seen of your powers, you could be, you know', I say.

'Well, thank you, O. May I call you O, by the way?'

'You may indeed. And what should I call you?' I ask.

'Will. "God's Will", some would say. But Will. You may call me Will, O.'

Will did not say he was *not* the Master, so he still could be.

'My expectation, Will,' I say, 'is that you know the reason I have come here.'

'I do. And you think I could help.'

'Well, I do. That's my hope.'

'This "other you", O: do you know what it could be like? Do you know what it is that you have come here to look for?'

'No.'

'Then let me tell you this: there are many things you could be. You could be a young lady in love.'

'I never did know', I say, 'if I *was* in love. As I now see it, I was not, not at all. Not with him, that is. You know, I have done all I could *not* to remember. Now, with you here—well, here and not quite here—I find I may do so, without the fear that memory will rede—'

'Go on, O.'

'—redeliver me to where I was. What is it? Something in how you speak, how your words come with such grace, and honesty—and, I would say, affection. You make me remember my father, and now I do not weep.'

'That is good to know, O. But this "other you": I could make it so that you *are* in love and have no doubt that you are in love.'

'In love with....'

'A youth with sweet eyes and a fair command of words. You would see each other, and that would be it. Head over heels. Joy. Ecstasy.'

'Would I have died by the end?'

'You would.'

I take a breath.

'Would *he?*' I ask.

'He would.'

'Then no, thank you.'

'But you have to think what death is, to such as you—and to such as him. You are not truly dead. You go on and on. I *made* you to go on and on. And you did say this yourself: There is a chorus of you, all over.'

'That's not quite what I meant', I say, but he's on a tear now.

'A chorus of you, and all of you make your way, your own way. You give answers to your brother and your father, and so on. You are a courtier's daughter, and so you have to be there—all of you, have to be—with the king and other observers at the play. You have to be bended out of form by the death of your father. And then you have to—again I say, all of you—do it all again. It goes on and on. There is no true death for you.'

'"Have to", you say. You say it all, with that.'

'There are other things I could make you: a saint; one close to another young lady; one in the clothes of a youth; a king, for you could indeed be a king—'

'You know what?' I say. 'I see this now. It's come to me. This is not the way for me to go on. I have no wish for you to make up "another me" for me. It's not "another me" I have to have; it's the true me. At last.'

'You are right, O. This is hard for me to say, but you are right.'

'I'll be on my way, then', I say. 'But before I go, I think I may have been given a mark, here, over my left eye, from when you rose up from the grave, if that's what you did. Do you have a glass, Will?'

'I may do. I'll look. But remember: You do not face yourself in a glass; you face yourself in yourself.'

Y

With these words of Will's the ground falls away from me. To look at it another way, the all of me rises.

I look at the ground, and there is no ground. I look to the left and to the right, and it's all gone: the mountain path I took on my way here, O-fie's Mountain, the home of the lady of the flowers and that of the two ladies that had to speak over each other, the King's Head—all of it.

I have been raised in to white, almost as it was before.

Have I died and gone to heaven?

There is no fear in me.

There is no expectancy. What will come will come when it will.

Time is still.

You are close to me now. I know you are close to me, which is to say that I know I have come close to you. I was the one that had to make my way. You have stayed where you are, but still been with me as I did so.

This other me: I did not see, could not see, that you would be the one to give me what I most wish for.

There was one lesson I had to give you before this. It was a lesson in how it was for me at home, with my father and brother, and with—but not with—the young lord, and in how I left one day, left it all and went on. On my own.

This now is another lesson, if you like, to make two.

It may be that there will be still another, for this is not the end, by no means the end. I have a long way to go from here.

Come on, you know what we have to do now. You have something I do not have. This is what I ask you now to give me.

Lay your hand on my words. Lay your hand on these words of mine as I speak them. I have come right up here, so close that you must know me to be here from my breath on that hand of yours. In, out; in, out: My breath. I see your hand. Look at it yourself. I have my own hand raised to yours. We are almost touching. It must be now. It must be now. Take that hand of mine and, with all your powers, draw me out.

Acknowledgements

The dedicatee of this book knows how much she contributed to it.

There are debts here also to (in order of appearance):

AMIENS (As You Like It)

BIANCA (The Taming of the Shrew)

CALIBAN (The Tempest)

DESDEMONA (Othello)

ENOBARBUS (Antony and Cleopatra)

FOOLS: Fool (King Lear), Feste (Twelfth Night), Elbow (Measure for Measure)

GHOSTS: Old Hamlet (Hamlet), others (Julius Caesar and Richard III)

HERO (Much Ado About Nothing)

IMOGEN (Cymbeline)

JULIET (Romeo and Juliet)

KINGS: Richard II, Henry IV, Henry V, Henry VI,

Edward IV, Edward V, Richard III, Henry VII, Henry VIII (history plays)
 LAERTES (Hamlet)
 MALVOLIO (Twelfth Night)
 NURSE (Romeo and Juliet)
 OFELIA (Hamlet, Quarto 1)
 PERICLES (Pericles Prince of Tyre)
 MISTRESS QUICKLY (Henry IV:1 and 2, Henry V and The Merry Wives of Windsor)
 PUCK, or ROBIN GOODFELLOW (A Midsummer Night's Dream)
 SHYLOCK (The Merchant of Venice), also the Book of Psalms (King James Version)
 TITANIA (A Midsummer Night's Dream)
 Uncanonical Text (Sir Thomas More)
 VALENTINE (The Two Gentlemen of Verona)

•

David and Ping Henningham would like to thank Sophie O'Neill, Rebecca Robinson, Jane Pike and Emily Tate at Inpress Books, Megan Simpkins at G.F Smith and Ken Edwards at Reality Street. Also Caroline Clark, Kevin Davey, David Collard, Oli Hazzard, Adam Mars-Jones and Philip Terry.

Supporting Cast

We are grateful to the following people for their
financial support towards this book:

FIRST FOLIO

Debra Chatfield · Nicolas Hodges · Wendy Whidden
Alan Teder · Trevor Bača · Tristan John · David Robins
Richard Furniss · David McMahon · Thomas Moody-Stuart
Anthony Brown · Bernard Moxham · Kevin Davey
Salvador Olvera Cháidez · Linda Shorey

SECOND QUARTO

Amy McCauley · Angela Creed · Emanuel Overbeeke
Nick Breeze · David Hebblethwaite · Patrick Ozzard-Low
Paul Fulcher · Tilmann Böttcher · Claire Allen · Sally Marks
Christian Mason · James Tookey · Kate Bland · Luke Lewis
Belle Claudi · Ty Bouque · Jonathan Cross · Vesna Main
Maureen Docherty · Jeremy Marshall · Matthew Gurewitsch
John Link · Barbara Hannigan · David Bremner · Judit Rajk

let me tell you

*"Paul Griffiths is one of a handful of fine writers
to find the secret passage leading from restriction
to richness."* – Adam Mars-Jones

Fifteen years after its first publication, the seminal novel *let me tell you* joins *Mr. Beethoven, The Tomb Guardians* and *let me go on* in our Paul Griffiths collection.

Ophelia tells her own story. Her account flows solely from the 481 words she speaks in *Hamlet*. This constraint hints at Ophelia's struggle against the limits placed upon her by her father, brother, Hamlet, and Shakespeare.

£12.99
ISBN: 9781916218666

Praise for *let me tell you*

'The reader will be captivated by Griffiths' touching portrait of Ophelia.' – Michael Miller, *New York Arts*

'An extraordinary work which extends our sense of what it is to be human beings.'
– John Goodby, *Wales Arts Review*

'The remarkable achievement is to extend Ophelia's world into impossible realms while remaining connected through deep feeling to her original. She resembles herself.' – Oli Hazzard, *Music & Literature*

'Ophelia shows that "there's more to me now than the poor, sweet daughter" in achingly lovely words that stem from Shakespeare but bring Beckett's later prose to mind.' – Boyd Tonkin, *The Independent*

'I found *let me tell you* a beautiful and enthralling work, as well as a great success in Oulipian terms.'
– Harry Mathews

'Line by line, then page by page, there is no sense of strain, just of a world, a voice, a story, beginning to emerge.' – Philip Terry, *Golden Handcuffs*

'*Let me tell you* is beautiful, philosophical and musical. It is a hymn to the human.' – Peter Hughes, *10th Muse*

'I was amazed by how moving and true Ophelia's voice is when up against and, surely thanks to, the constraint.' – Caroline Clark, author of *Own Sweet Time*

'Griffiths trusts that his form will effect its own kind of "saying." That it results in a character with emotional depth that plausibly develops a life story about which *Hamlet* is otherwise silent only validates the wisdom of the author's commitment to that form.' – Daniel Green, *The Reading Experience*

'Griffiths' work as music critic and translator shines through; he has composed a prose work whose components recur and resound like familiar notes.' – Alyssa Pelish, *Rain Taxi*

'*Let me tell you* showed that a well-chosen constraint could be generative, musical, and astonishingly creative.' – Kevin Davey, author of *Playing Possum*

'Ophelia's haunting, incantatory monologue is deeply moving.' – David Collard, author of *Multiple Joyce*

Henningham Family Press

Since 2006, our studio has been a microbrewery for books.

Our ingenious handmade editions can be found in the V&A, National Galleries Scotland, National Poetry Library, the Tate, and Stanford University collections.

Our performance publishing events compress the creation of printed matter into hectic live-art events.

Now our Fiction brings you authors who are re-inventing the conventions of Modern writing.

CLAIRE ALLEN
The Blackbird

PAUL GRIFFITHS
Mr. Beethoven
The Tomb Guardians
let me tell you
let me go on

SOPHIE HERXHEIMER
60 Lovers to Make and Do
Your Candle Accompanies
The Sun
The Listening Forest

CHRIS MCCABE
Dedalus
Mud

J. O. MORGAN
Pupa

PASCAL O'LOUGHLIN
Now Legwarmers
The Goddess Lens

YISMAKE WORKU
The Lost Spell
(tr. Bethlehem Attfield)

About the Author

Paul Griffiths is an internationally respected music critic and librettist. His books have been translated into eleven languages.

He has worked as a music critic for *The Times*, *The New York Times* and *The New Yorker*. He received an OBE for services to music literature and composition, and has been honoured also in France (Chevalier dans l'Ordre des Arts et des Lettres) and the United States (Member of the American Academy of Arts and Sciences).

Extracts from his third novel, *let me tell you*, were made into a song cycle by Hans Abrahamsen in 2013 for Barbara Hannigan and the Berlin Philharmonic Orchestra and collected in *The Penguin Book of Oulipo*.

His fourth novel, *Mr. Beethoven*, was shortlisted for the Goldsmiths Prize 2020, longlisted for the Walter Scott Prize & Republic of Consciousness Prize 2021, and republished in the United States by NYRB Books.